THEY FLEW ALONE

GEORGE SULLIVAN

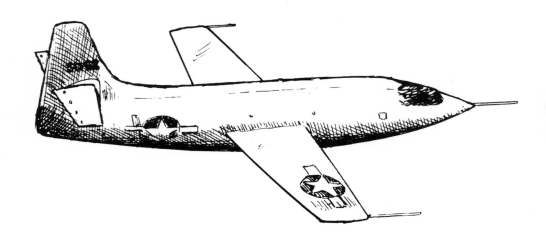

THEY FLEW ALONE

ILLUSTRATED BY SERGE HOLLERBACH

FREDERICK WARNE & CO., INC.

NEW YORK AND

LONDON

ACKNOWLEDGMENTS

I am grateful to countless people who helped to make this book possible. Special thanks are due to Eugene Baker for providing the opportunity to consult the aeronautical library of the late E. N. Pickerill, Secretary of the Early Birds of Aviation; the New York Public Library; the National Library of the Australian Consulate-General, New York; the Directorate of Information Services, Office of the Assistant Secretary of Defense; and the Public Relations Department, United Aircraft Corporation, Hartford, Connecticut.

INTRODUCTION

The airplane is only a machine. Its success was spurred by the human spirit. It could never have spanned oceans and continents, could not even have risen from the ground, without the hand of man at the controls and the mind of man commanding its course.

Through all of aviation, from the time of the first balloonists right up until the present day, many of the most significant flights were made by individuals, by men sealed alone in tiny cockpits. This book tells of some of them—of Wilbur Wright, the first man to achieve powered flight; of Louis Blériot, the first man to cross the English Channel and of Lindbergh. It also tells of a number of latter-day flights, the first in a jet and the first through the sound barrier.

A few of the chapters concern the exploits of men who, strictly speaking, did not "fly alone." These include the story of Alcock and Brown, the first men to cross the Atlantic Ocean non-stop, and Kingsford-Smith and Ulm, the first men to span the Pacific. These men are included because they, as much as Wright, Blériot, Lindbergh and the others, exemplified the indomitable spirit that made the airplane a success.

GLOSSARY OF AERONAUTICAL TERMS

AERODYNAMICS—The mechanical science that deals with the motion of air and the effects of such motion on an aircraft's surfaces.

AILERON—A hinged, movable surface, usually at the trailing (rear) edge of an airplane's wing, that controls the roll of the aircraft.

BIPLANE—An airplane with two sets of wings, one above—and usually slightly forward—of the other.

BOMB BAY—An area in the underside of the fuselage, usually equipped with doors, through which bombs may be dropped.

CAMBER—The rise of the curve of an airplane's wing or other surface.

CEILING—Height of the lower level of a bank of clouds above the ground.

CHOCK—A block or truss of wood or metal which, when placed in front of the wheels of an airplane while on the ground, serves to prevent the forward movement of the aircraft.

CONTROL STICK—The vertical lever that controls the elevator and ailerons. (The elevator is operated by a forward-and-back movement of the stick; the ailerons by side-to-side movement.)

COWLING—A removable covering.

DIESEL ENGINE—An engine designed by the German, Rudolf Diesel, using compression of fuel as its ignition system.

DIHEDRAL—The angle at which the right or left wing of an aircraft is inclined upward or downward from the horizontal.

DIRIGIBLE—A lighter-than-air-craft; an airship.

DRIFT—The deviation of an aircraft from its set course due to cross winds.

ELEVATOR—A movable surface, usually at the trailing edge (rear) of the stabilizer; used to direct the climb or dive of the aircraft.

FLAPS—The hinged surfaces usually on the underside of an aircraft's wings which, when lowered, increase the lifting power of the wings and thus enable the aircraft to fly more slowly yet remain stable.

FUSELAGE—The complete central structure of an aircraft to which the wings, tail surfaces, engines, etc., are attached.

GROUND LOOP—An abrupt turn on the part of the aircraft while taxiing, or during a landing or takeoff run.

KNOT—A velocity of one nautical mile per hour.

LIFT—The aerodynamic forces upon the aircraft's wings and stabilizer which cause the craft to stay aloft.

MONOPLANE—An airplane with but one wing or set of wings.

NACELLE—The structure that houses an aircraft's engine.

PITCH—The nosing of an aircraft up or down from its longitudinal axis.

POINT OF NO RETURN—That point in a flight that occurs as soon as the midpoint is passed.

PROPELLER—A device with a revolving hub and radiating blades that is driven by the airplane's engine.

PROPELLER, PUSHER—A propeller that is mounted on the rear end of the engine or propeller shaft.

PROPELLER, TRACTOR—A propeller mounted on the forward end of the engine or propeller shaft.

R.P.M.—Revolutions per minute (of an aircraft's engine).

ROLL—The rotation of the airplane about the axis of the fuselage.

RUDDER—A movable control surface attached to the vertical stabilizer and located at the rear of the airplane; used in combination with the ailerons to turn the aircraft.

SQUALL—A sudden storm of brief duration.

STABILIZER—The fixed horizontal tail surface of an airplane.

STRUTS—The vertical structural members of an aircraft used to brace or support.

SUPERCHARGER—A pump for forcing air into an aircraft's engine in order to increase fuel ignition and thereby engine power.

TAXI—To operate an airplane under its own power, either on land or water.

TRIM TAB—A small moveable surface set in the trailing edge of an aileron, elevator or rudder and designed to aid in controlling or stabilizing the aircraft.

UNDERCARRIAGE—The main wheels, skids or floats and their supports; the landing gear.

VERY PISTOL—A pistol used to fire colored signal flares.

WARP—To change the form of a wing by twisting it. Warping was formerly used to perform the function now performed by ailerons.

YAW—To deviate sideways from a straight course.

CONTENTS

THEY FLEW ALONE

CHAPTER 1
GENIUS AT KITTY HAWK

The story of Orville and Wilbur Wright has been told many times, but no book that deals with the history of aviation can overlook them; for, indeed, they wrought a miracle at Kitty Hawk.

Some people lose sight of precisely what the Wrights did achieve, however. As every schoolboy knows, they are remembered as the first men to attain powered flight. Yet this event, while of landmark proportions, was something of an anticlimax.

The great genius of the Wrights was that they were the first to achieve stability in the air, to turn and maneuver by means of a unique system of controls based upon their aerodynamic research. They unlocked these secrets at Kitty Hawk in 1902, a full year before their motor-powered machine was ready to fly. On that cold December day in 1903 when their engine-driven plane took to the air for the first time, it was merely further confirmation of their findings.

Wilbur Wright was born in Millville, Indiana, in 1867, and Orville was born in Dayton, Ohio, four years later. They had two older brothers and a sister. Their father, Milton Wright, was shifted about frequently in his duties as a bishop in the United Brethren Church. The family moved from Indiana to Ohio, then to Iowa, then back to Indiana before finally settling down in Ohio, in Dayton.

Orville and Wilbur are said to have inherited their

mechanical ability from their mother, Susan Koerner Wright. She was an inventive woman, always devising ingenious kitchen utensils. Her family described her as "a mother who could mend anything." She died before her two sons had become seriously interested in flight, otherwise she might have made helpful contributions to their work.

From their earliest childhood, the Wrights were interested in things mechanical. One of young Orville's most prized possessions was a gyroscope top that he received on his fifth birthday. And there is more evidence. One day Orville's mother sent him off to kindergarten. Later she was astonished to learn that he never reached school. He had stopped off at the home of a neighborhood chum, and became so fascinated by a sewing machine that he forgot all about school.

One day the boys' father brought home a small helicopter type of toy that would lift into the air by virtue of power it derived from a twisted rubber band. This toy was their introduction to the subject of flight. The boys were fascinated by the plaything and built several copies. They managed to get each one to fly almost as well as the original. But when they built a very large version of the toy, they could not get it to rise from the ground. This setback marked an end to their first experiments.

Neither Wilbur or Orville ever went to college. In fact, neither received a high school diploma, although each attended school full time. Wilbur attended high school in Richmond, Indiana, but moved away just before graduation. It was necessary for him to be present at school on commencement day in order to receive a diploma, but the family did not feel it was reason enough for a trip. Orville, in his final year in high school, took special courses to prepare for college. These, however, were not the prescribed courses; and although he learned more than many of his classmates, Orville, like his brother, was never awarded a diploma.

When the boys were growing up, Wilbur naturally looked upon Orville as his "kid brother." Yet, according to Fred C. Kelly, the authorized biographer of the pair, there was always "great devotion and understanding between them." During the winter of his senior year in high school, Wilbur was hurt playing shinny, a primitive form of ice hockey. The injury forced him to reduce his physical activity for many years. Thus, it was Wilbur who did the bulk of the reading, writing and planning. Orville was the more active member of the duo and did most of the physical work.

Often they could be found making things in their small home workshop. They built a printing press and published a four-page weekly newspaper called the *West Side News*. Their next interest was bicycles. At first they merely raced them, but in 1892, they founded the Wright Cycle Company "to sell, repair and manufacture bicycles." Business was good from the start and they profited.

In 1896, the boys read of the work of Otto Lilienthal, a German who had mastered the art of gliding flight. Lilienthal was to be an inspiring influence upon the Wrights.

Otto had begun experimenting with flying in 1861 when he was thirteen years old, and he soon interested his brother Gustave in his hobby. In his first efforts, Otto would attempt to glide by running down a steep hill with light wings fastened to his arms. He realized that in order to achieve a straight and sustained glide, he would have to learn a great deal more about the basic characteristics of flight. His avocation blossomed into long years of scientific study and experiment.

Otto began by observing the flight of birds. He kept a number of young storks and watched carefully as they made their first attempts to fly. They did not fly naturally nor from instinct, he noted; they had to practice. It took several days of trial and error experimentation before a bird could take to the air. Lilienthal observed that the stork always faced into the wind when attempting to fly. He noticed how the bird varied the camber of its wings to get increased lift, and how it could change the size of the angle between its wing and body—called the dihedral—to get more stability. All of this information was to prove of immense value.

In 1894, Lilienthal built a cone-shaped hill from which to conduct his glider flights. The hill was fifty feet high and sloped in all directions. Thus, no matter from which direction the wind blew, he could make use of it.

Lilienthal succeeded in making flights of up to 300 yards in length. The apparatus which held him aloft was called a "hang glider" and consisted of a pair of wings and a tail made of willow struts over which waxed cotton cloth had been stretched. Otto passed his head through a central opening and took firm hold. Sometimes he was able to soar to a greater height than his starting point. He could change course to the right or left and even negotiate a full 180 degree turn simply by moving his body within the opening so as to shift his center of gravity.

Lilienthal's experiments ended in tragedy. In August 1896, while testing a new rudder in a high wind, his glider went into a sudden nosedive from the height of about one hundred feet. He was seriously injured and died the next day. His brother Gustave discontinued any further experimentation.

"It was my greatest wish that a great number of young people will devote their attention to my apparatus," Lilienthal once wrote. ". . . I myself am too old." The wish was to be fulfilled. Lilienthal published the results of his experiments in a book entitled, *Problem of Flying and Practical Experiments in Soaring.* In 1899, Wilbur Wright wrote a letter to the Smithsonian Institution in Washington, D.C., and requested publications on the subject of flight. One of those sent to him was the Lilienthal work. His experimentation had not been in vain.

The Wrights were also greatly influenced by Octave Chanute, an American pioneer in gliding flight. More than one-thousand flights were made in Chanute gliders between 1896 and 1897, all by assistants as pilots. Chanute, then in his sixties, was too old for the risks and rigors of flying. The Wrights considered Chanute's book, *Progress in Flying Machines,* to be the best written history of man's attempt to fly.

Chanute and the Wrights became close friends. He was one of the first to realize the great significance of the Wrights' experiments. Once or twice when the Wrights were discouraged and considered abandoning their plans, Chanute was the one who spurred them on. He told them that they knew more than anyone else in the world about flying and that in the interest of science they must continue.

The Wrights used the profits from the bicycle business to build up their library on aeronautical subjects. They made some outdoor experiments with kites and, in 1899, built their first glider. It cost $15.00.

Despite its lack of elegance, the first glider employed a unique scientific principle, one that triggered an important breakthrough in the means of controlling flight. Whereas Lilienthal had sought to keep his gliders level by bodily gymnastics, the Wrights made the glider itself do the work. Wilbur was the first to grasp the principle, and he demonstrated it to his brother by means of a simple experiment. Taking the opposite ends of a small cardboard box, he gave it a spherical twist. The top and bottom sides of the box warped in such a way that they each presented different angles at opposite ends. Yet the structural integrity of the box was not harmed. This principle, when applied to the wings of a biplane, was used by the Wrights to control their craft's lateral movement. Ultimately, the knowledge of this principle led to the development of ailerons, the hinged or moveable portion of a plane's wing which enables it to bank or roll.

Another innovation of the Wright glider was that it allowed the pilot to lie flat upon it, thus exposing much less of his body surface to the passing air. A horizontal elevator mounted in front of the pilot enabled him to control the plane's lengthwise stability.

The Wrights were very enthusiastic about their craft and, when blessed with the proper amount of wind, they expected that it would stay in the air for hours at a time. They learned from the U.S. Weather Bureau that the Atlantic shore of North Carolina offered some of the stiffest, steadiest winds in the country; so in September of 1900, they took their glider to Kitty Hawk. It flew, but not nearly so well as they had anticipated. The control systems performed as well as they had hoped, but the lifting capability of the craft was a disappointment.

The Wrights built a second glider, somewhat larger than the first, and in 1901, returned to Kitty Hawk. This one too fell short of their hopes. They decided that their failure was due in part to the existing scientific data upon which they had based their calculations. For instance, they now believed that Lilienthal's tables of air pressure were wholly inaccurate. "... after two years of experiments, we cast all aside ... ," Wilbur was to write. "Truth and error were everywhere so intimably mixed as to be indistinguishable."

The brothers temporarily shelved plans to build a third glider, and began months of tedious research to acquire the scientific information that they needed. They built a wind tunnel, and although crude by today's standards—it was little more than a rectangular box, with the wind provided by a fan powered by a one-cylinder gas engine—it helped them develop a whole new world of scientific data. They cut out and tested tiny, sheet-metal wings of more than two-hundred shapes and sizes, arranged in monoplane, biplane and triplane combinations. They found that the single surface wing gave the most efficient lift, but they continued to favor the biplane because of its sturdiness.

These experiments lasted until late in the summer of 1902, when the Wrights returned to Kitty Hawk with a third glider—one they felt to be of improved design. Indeed it was. It boasted improvements in the wing-warping controls and rudder and elevator mechanism. Its gull-shaped wings, much larger than those in the previous models, had a span of 32 feet, and 305 square feet of surface. They made hundreds of glides in the craft and achieved smooth, banked turns that were sheer artistry. Always before it had been thought that a plane steers the way a ship steers—by means of a rudder. But with their third glider, the Wrights found this to be false. They learned that a plane steers in somewhat the same way a skater steers when whizzing along the ice. When the skater leans to the left, he turns left. Leaning to the right makes him turn right. By warping the wings of their glider, the Wrights could lean their plane —and tilt and turn it.

During these trials they made one run of fewer than 200 yards, but still a record. They now felt that they had thoroughly mastered gliding flight. They were ready to take another step forward and attempt powered flight.

When they returned to Dayton, the Wrights set to work to develop an engine. What they did was to take an automobile engine apart and put it back together again, using aluminum parts in place of heavier steel ones wherever they could. They tried many different combinations before they finally arrived at a 240-pound engine that delivered thirteen horsepower, which they judged to be enough to get their 650-pound airplane into the air.

The design of the propeller was a special problem. After all, virtually no research had ever been done on the subject of propellers for aircraft, and what information did exist was contradictory. They went back to the aerodynamic tables that they had evolved from their wind tunnel experiments. From studying these tables, they were able to design propellers—they used two of them—with the right pitch and proper blade area. They were constructed of wood, hand-finished, varnished and highly polished. Each one measured eight feet in length and was turned by means of a chain hookup with the engine.

Once they knew the size, weight and power of their engine, the Wrights were able to calculate the dimensions for their new plane. It was a smart-looking biplane; they called it the *Flyer*. It was worked out with such precision that they computed that the weight of the engine, right of center, would be thirty-four pounds more than the pilot who would be lying beside it, left of center. They made the right wing four inches longer than the left, which gave additional and compensating lift on the right side. The wings spanned forty-five feet, four inches. The controls were the same as in the 1902 machine.

When the Wrights returned to Kitty Hawk in September 1903, they found that heavy storms had wrecked their hangar, so they set to work making repairs. The *Flyer*, with the pilot aboard, weighed about one thousand pounds, much too heavy to be launched without assistance. To facilitate the launching, the Wrights planned to use a single rail track. It was sixty feet long and made of wood and covered with greased sheet-iron strips.

A small two-wheeled truck ran on the track, and a plank was laid across the truck. The sledlike skids of the plane (it had no wheels) rested upon he plank. The idea, of course, was to have the airplane race down the track and lift into the air, leaving the plank and truck behind.

By December 14, everything was ready for the first flight. Five men from the Kill Devil lifesaving station helped the brothers lay the track down the gentle slope of the Kill Devil dune, positioning it so that the biplane would be facing into the wind. Wilbur and Orville tossed a coin to see which one would serve as pilot. Wilbur won and started the engine. The machine rushed down the track and began to rise. It held in the air for only a second or two, then veered to one side, scraping the ground and causing some structural damage. Wilbur had made a mistake in handling the controls and blamed himself, not the machine, for the flight's failure. Repairs had to be made before another trial could be attempted.

The next flight was made on December 17. The day was bitter cold and the shore was raked by icy gusts of up to 27 miles an hour. There was no need to use the dune; they laid the track on the level ground near their campsite.

Now it was Orville's turn. He got in position on the lower wing at 10:30 A.M. and ordered the engine started. The machine started slowly, then gathered speed.

This time there was no mishap. The machine raced down the track. Wilbur ran alongside for about forty feet, then watched breathlessly as it lifted into the air.

The plane was four feet in the air by the time it reached the end of the track. Orville proved a good pilot. He kept the machine in the air for twelve seconds, covering 120 feet.

"The flight lasted only twelve seconds," Orville was to write ten years later, "but it was nevertheless the first in the history of the world in which a machine marrying a man had raised itself by its own power into the air in full flight, had sailed forward without reduction of speed, and had finally landed at a point as high as that from which it started."

A handful of spectators witnessed the flight. They were John T. Daniels, W. S. Dough, and E. D. Etheridge, friends of the Wrights from the lifesaving station. W. C. Brinkley had walked over from nearby Manteo, and another observer was Johnny Moore, a schoolboy from Nags Head, North Carolina.

The first flight was recorded by a camera, too. Orville estimated at what point the machine would leave the ground, focused his camera accordingly, then instructed John Daniels in how to aim it and trip the shutter.

In inspecting the plane after its flight, the brothers discovered that a lever for controlling the engine was damaged and one of the skids was cracked. They repaired this damage in about twenty minutes, and then brought the machine back to its starting point.

It was Wilbur's turn again. This time he was more successful than he had been a few days previous and managed to keep the machine in the air for 175 feet.

Orville was back at the controls for a third flight made shortly before noon. He achieved a height of fourteen feet and a distance of 175 feet.

The fourth flight of the day was the most sensational. Wilbur piloted the machine a distance of 852 feet. He remained in the air for fifty-nine seconds.

After their four successful flights, the Wrights felt certain that all they needed was practice in order to be able to go much higher and much farther. They were discussing whether they should attempt to fly the four miles to the Kitty Hawk weather station to use up the gasoline that remained in the *Flyer's* tank, when a sudden gust of wind caught the machine and turned it over. Daniels tried to grab the spars to hold it, but the wind was too strong, and Daniels was badly bruised.

The wind caused serious damage to the engine and propeller chains, and several struts and many ribs were broken. It was apparent that no more flights could be attempted that season. The craft was dismantled and shipped back to Dayton.

On May 22, 1906, the U.S. Patent Office recognized the Wrights' claims and specifications for warping the wing tips and swinging the rudders to maintain stability in the air, and they were granted Patent No. 831,393. Significantly, they had applied for this patent on March 23, 1903, nine months before the attempt at powered flight was made.

The Wright saga has a remarkable footnote to it. The public, the government, and the press in the United States hardly noticed what the Wrights had done for the better part of a decade.

Immediately after the first flight, the brothers wired their father in Dayton and asked him to "inform press." Their older brother, Lorin, went to the local newspaper office and told the editor that Orville had taken their flying machine into the air for fifty-nine seconds.

The editor just laughed. "Now if it had been fifty-nine *minutes*," he said, "that would be news."

The Norfolk *Virginian-Pilot* and the Cincinnati *Enquirer* were two of the handful of papers that bothered to carry news of the Wrights' triumphs at Kitty Hawk. But the story that appeared was inaccurate, even fanciful. It stated that the Wrights' plane flew three miles out over the ocean and back, and that the craft was powered by two propellers, one in the back to push it forward, and one underneath to keep it aloft.

As late as 1907, in their own city of Dayton, the newspapers were not quite sure who the Wrights were or what they had invented. The Dayton *Herald* for March 21 of that year referred to them as "inventors of the airship," and Orville's name was given as "Oliver."

Wilbur Wright used to enjoy telling about a conversation he once overheard while riding a Dayton sreetcar not far from the field where his brother was conducting test flights. This incident took place several years after the successes at Kitty Hawk. A local resident and a visitor from out of town were chatting when suddenly Orville's plane roared overhead.

"My God!" screamed the visitor, "What's that?"

"It ain't nothing at all," said the native, and he hardly bothered to glance skyward. "It's just one of them crazy boys we got here by the name of Wright. Darn fools have been trying to make a machine that can fly. They oughta know you can't go against nature."

In spite of the lack of recognition, the Wrights continued to perfect their airplane and increase their skill as fliers. In 1904, they flew the first full circle. In 1905, they flew continuously for a distance of 24 miles. The same year they offered their invention to the U.S. Government "for use in war," but the War Department showed little interest. The Wrights then turned to Europe, hoping to interest a foreign government in what they had achieved. They did obtain a contract from a French syndicate for demonstration flights and the purchase of an airplane. Their test flights in Europe were startlingly successful; they were hailed everywhere abroad as the conquerors of the air. The U.S. Signal Corps then became interested in he Wrights' work and general acclaim in the United States soon followed.

It was not until 1948, the forty-fifth anniversary of the flights at Kitty Hawk, that the Smithsonian Institution accepted the *Flyer* for exhibition. A card placed on the plane served as fitting summation of the Wrights' careers. It read: "The world's first power-driven machine in which man made free controlled and sustained flight . . . By original scientific research, the Wright brothers discovered the principles of human flight as inventors, builders and flyers. They further developed the aeroplane, taught men to fly, and opened the era of aviation."

CHAPTER

2
FIRST
FLIGHT
IN
EUROPE

When Alberto Santos-Dumont was a child, he often played a game called "flying birds." Boys and girls, seated in a circle, would raise their hands whenever the person conducting the game made a false statement. "A chicken can fly." "A pigeon can fly." No hands went up. "A man can fly." Santos-Dumont did not raise his hand. He believed the statement to be correct. He believed that one day men would fly.

The son of a wealthy Brazilian coffee planter, Santos-Dumont was in his teens when he arrived in Paris in 1891. There he became an enthusiastic ballonist, and Parisians soon got used to the sight of him soaring above the rooftops or, on his less fortunate days, getting a ducking in the Seine.

He became one of Europe's foremost authorities on lighter-than-air craft. Even his first balloon was significant. To keep its weight down, he ordered the airbag to be made of a filmy Japanese silk. Professional balloon-makers of the day laughed, but silk proved stronger than any of the ordinarily used materials, and soon other balloonists began to use silk, too.

His next step was to build a dirigible, that is, a torpedo-shaped balloon that could be steered. He fitted it out with a twelve-horsepower automobile engine. Beneath the airbag, he built a long, narrow catwalk. He could make the airship rise or dip by positioning himself forward or aft on the catwalk. A triangular-shaped rudder permitted him to steer either right or left. Santos-Dumont's airship did not drift aimlessly like others of the day. He could control flight.

Santos-Dumont built dirigible after dirigible—sixteen in all, improving his theories with each one. His first airship careened into a grove of trees after rising and was damaged beyond repair. In dirigible No. 2, the airbag collapsed, a mishap that almost cost him his life. He did not achieve consistent success until he had built his fourth airship. This one got to be a familiar sight over the Bois de Boulogne. Parisian taxicab drivers, upon seeing him hover into sight, would stop and wave. "Vive Santos!" people would cry.

Henry Deutsch, a wealthy founder of the Aero Club of France, offered purse of 100,000 francs to the first person who could fly from the Aero Club field, around the Eiffel Tower and back—a distance of seven miles. The time alloted was thirty minutes. Santos-Dumont tried to win the prize—many times.

He made his first attempt in dirigible No. 4. He rounded the tower and was headed back when the engine failed. In another try, his suspension ropes fouled in the propeller, and he had to cut the engine. This left him at the mercy of the wind, which swept the airship off course and onto a hotel roof. The dirigible was smashed to pieces, but firemen rescued Santos-Dumont.

On October 18, 1901, he tried for the prize a third time, with dirigible No. 6. A smart wind astern carried him toward the tower at a rapid clip, but a guide rope caught on a rooftop causing the balloon to take a frightening dip. Spectators rushed up and unhooked the rope allowing the airship to resume its flight. Santos-Dumont had circled the tower and was heading back when the engine stopped. He crawled out on the keel and repaired it with a pair of pliers, but the incident cost him precious minutes. He crossed the finish line with the time limit, but the thirty seconds it took him to descend brought him over the thirty-minute mark. The Aero Club ruled, therefore, that he was not eligible for the prize; but the press and public outcry was so great that the Aero Club reversed its decision two weeks later. Santos-Dumont distributed the prize among the poor of Paris.

Within a few years after Santos-Dumont had first demonstrated that controlled flight was possible, interest in dirigibles became international in scope. Many people believed that lighter-than-air craft would one day be the world's principal means of carrying passengers and freight.

While in the midst of his balloon experiments, Santos-Dumont heard rumors that the Wright Brothers were making long, sustained glider flights near their home in Dayton. Most people of the day paid these stories little heed. Not Santos-Dumont. He felt they were true, and he began studying the principles of gliding flight. He enlisted the help of Gabriel Voisin, who had flown a Wright glider from the sand hills at Berck, on the channel coast.

Voisin, like many French aviation pioneers, had come under the influence of Lawrence Hargrave, an Australian. Hargrave had begun experimenting with ornithopters—machines powered by flapping wings—as early as 1884. He achieved flights of several hundred feet with these weird devices, then turned to work with box kites, oblong-shaped kites that consisted of a wooden framework covered with fabric except at the ends and the middle. Hargrave learned that if he curved the surfaces of these structures, they developed almost twice the lift of those with flat surfaces.

Santos-Dumont's first gliders were closely styled after Hargrave's kites. He used a unique method for getting them aloft. He would mount the glider on a float which was towed by a motorboat. When the boat got up enough speed. the glider would climb into the air. Santos-Dumont would stay airborne for a few seconds, then dip into the river. He also experimented with a glider towed by an airship. The same year—1905— he built his first airplane.

This, like his gliders, showed clearly Hargrave's influence. The wings

resembled two huge box kites, joined together end to end. They spanned forty feet. A third box kite formed the tail, and this was connected to the wing by a frame of bamboo struts. The machine weighed 645 pounds. Perhaps the most remarkable feature of the machine was that it flew tail-first.

The eight-cylinder engine was mounted between the wings, along with its pusher propeller. Two bicycle wheels, set in standard cycle forks and fixed to the fuselage below the pilot's nacelle, served as the landing gear.

To control the machine, Santos-Dumont adjusted the surface panels of the tail kite, manipulating them right or left, up or down. He also helped to maintain stability by the use of moveable planes or "curtains" in the outer wing struts. He called his plane the *14 Bis.* On August 22, 1906, he hauled the machine to the Bagatelle cavalry field, fixed it to the framework of a late model dirigible, and then took the airship aloft. Once high enough, Santos-Dumont released the airplane, and flew it back to earth under its own power. It was a unique stunt, to be sure, although the experiment could scarcely be called an acceptable heavier-than-air trial. It was an encouraging first step, however, and set the stage for flights of a more conventional nature.

Santos-Dumont continued to experiment with his plane during the summer of 1906, making short "hops"—and that is just what they were —of several feet a number of times. He then notified the Aero Club of France that he planned to try for a 3,000 franc prize that was being offered by Ernest Archdeacon for the first flight in Europe of more than 25 meters (about 78-feet). He set October 23 as the date.

A huge crowd gathered at the Bagatelle Field to watch the demonstration. A mechanic spun the propeller. The engine's loud, staccato bursts ripped the air. Santos-Dumont made a few tentative starts, then urged the bizarre craft across the field. A chorus of "oohs" and "ahs" rose from the crowd as the wheels lost contact with the earth. Then abruptly, as if someone had swatted it with a giant club, the spindly machine of bamboo and cloth fell to the earth, completely wrecking itself. Santos-Dumont climbed out unhurt.

The crowd cheered their approval. They had seen an airplane fly, however short the distance. The Brazilian salvaged what parts he could and built a new airplane. On November 12, he was ready to try again. This time results were much better. He made three flights, and according to the judges of Aero Club, the longest was 720 feet and lasted twenty-one seconds.

Santos-Dumont was acclaimed a national hero. All of France went wild with excitement. (Few people knew of the triumphs that the Wrights had achieved, that three years earlier they had flown at Kitty Hawk and stayed up twice as long.) Santos-Dumont was awarded the medal of the Legion of Honor. A London paper headlined: "The First Flight of a Machine Heavier-Than-Air!" The Paris edition of the New York *Herald* agreed, calling this "the first mechanical flight of man." Thomas Edison, the scientific wizard of the day, added to the applause and sent Santos-Dumont an autographed picture. "To Santos-Dumont," read the inscription, "the Pioneer of the Air . . . Homage from Edison."

The Wrights were not restored to their rightful place in aviation history until 1908.

That year they made a series of wondrous flights at Le Mans, about 125-miles from Paris, clearly demonstrating their superiority over all other airmen of the day. Only then did the average Frenchman grant that the Wright's had undoubtedly flown as early as 1903. Santos-Dumont accepted this fact, too, and the realization that he was merely the first man *in Europe* to fly.

Santos-Dumont was also the first man to take off from the ground without human assistance, and using the plane's undercarriage. The Wrights, recall, used a track and a primitive catapult system.

The work of Santos-Dumont triggered a surge of interest in aviation. After the Brazilian came Louis Blériot, Leon Delagrange, and Henri Farman. All made successful flights, and Farman piloted the first airplane in Europe to complete a flight of one-kilometer, a distance of five-eighths of a mile.

Santos-Dumont gained headlines again in 1908 with a plane he called the *Demoiselle*. A tiny machine, it had a wing span of only eighteen feet, and, weighing about 259 pounds, it was lighter than the average motorcycle of the day. The machine was powered by a twenty-eight horsepower water-cooled engine, and control was achieved by means of a wing-warping principle. Its landing gear was three bicycle wheels.

Santos-Dumont made flights in the *Demoiselle* at speeds of up to sixty miles an hour. This was a record, easily surpassing the best that the Wrights had done.

Santos-Dumont's experiments in aeronautics continued until 1928. At that time he was trying to build a diesel engine for airplanes. He returned to Brazil that year, and the government declared a national holiday to celebrate his arrival.

Santos-Dumont never took out any patents on his airplane designs. What he had learned was free for all to use. His most prized possession was a gold medal that he received from the Brazilian government. It was inscribed with these words: "Por ceos nunca d'antes navegados."—"Through skies never before navigated." For Santos-Dumont, that was satisfaction enough.

CHAPTER
3
CROSSING
THE
CHANNEL

One man who realized the deep importance of the Santos-Dumont flight was Lord Northcliffe, owner of the London *Daily Mail*, a man later to be known as the "Father of British Aviation." In November 1906, his newspaper carried this editorial:

"The air around London and other large cities will be darkened by the flight of aeroplanes. New difficulties of every kind will arise, not the least being the military problem caused by the virtual annihilation of frontiers and the acquisition of power to pass readily through the air above the sea. The isolation of the United Kingdom may disappear and the success of M. Santos-Dumont has an international significance. They are not mere dreamers who hold that the time is at hand when air power will be even more important than sea power."

This commentary was only one aspect of Lord Northcliffe's campaign to goad the British into building up their aviation industry. Late in 1906, he put forward the first of a number of purses for individuals willing to demonstrate skill and daring in flying airplanes. The first was a prize of 10,000 pounds (about $50,000 at the time) for the first person to fly from London to Manchester, a distance of about 150 miles. Such a feat was then considered well beyond possibility, and competing newspapers jeered at Northcliffe's offer. *Punch* ridiculed Northcliffe with the announcement of three purses of 10,000 pounds one to go to the first person to fly to

Mars and back in a week, the second to the man who could reach the center of the earth in a fortnight, and the third to the person who could swim from Fishguard in Wales to Sandy Hook on the New Jersey coast within the ensuing two weeks. The fast-paced development of aviation soon stilled this sort of talk, however, and in less than four years the London to Manchester flight was to become a reality.

In 1908, after Wilbur Wright had completed a series of spectacularly successful flights at Le Mans, flights that surmounted every existing European speed and distance record, Lord Northcliffe announced the *Daily Mail* prize of 500 pounds to the first pilot to make a crossing of the English Channel. The following year he increased the purse to 1,000 pounds. Soon after, several pilots began preparations to make the Channel crossing.

Money was not their only incentive; enduring fame was another. In the mind of every European, the English Channel, twenty-one miles across at its narrowest point, was Great Britain's special safeguard, and, as such, one of the most formidable barriers of all time. Surely, great and lasting eminence would fall upon the first man to make the crossing by air.

Attempts began in earnest in 1909. By mid-summer of that year several camps had been pitched behind the French channel cliffs near Calais, with an aircraft the feature of each campsite. Hubert Latham was at Sangatte, while Louis Blériot set up operations a few miles away at Les Barraques. The Count de Lambert established a base at Wissant. Here he set to work assembling a biplane he had purchased from the Wrights. The craft was demolished in a practice flight, abruptly ending the count's role as a competitor.

Latham was the first to try. A dapper young Frenchman with English blood in his veins, Latham had won renown in several areas of sport. He had flown the Channel by balloon in 1904, crossing from London to Paris. He enjoyed big game hunting and auto racing. While racing speedboats at Monte Carlo, Latham met Léon Levavasseur, the designer of the sleek *Antoinette*, an 8-cylinder, 55-horsepower monoplane. Latham first soloed in the craft in April 1909, and by summer he felt ready for the Channel venture.

Once Latham notified the *Daily Mail* that he was about to seek Lord Northcliffe's prize, enthusiasm was aroused on both sides of the Straits of Dover. Crowds flocked to the camp at Sangatte hoping to catch a glimpse of Latham, a pilot so bold that he would risk a flight over open water. Not the Wright Brothers, not Santos-Dumont, no one, in fact, had demonstrated this particular brand of courage. Every day steamers brought throngs of excursionists and great numbers of journalists and photographers to the French shore. The French government assigned a torpedo destroyer, the *Harpon*, to follow Latham's flight. In mid-July the vessel dropped anchor a few miles off the cliffs near Sangatte to await the attempt.

Early in the morning of July 19, 1909, Latham decided that the moment had come. Although there was a haze that obscured the fabled white chalk cliffs of Dover in the distance, visibility was ten miles. The sun shone brightly; the Channel was as smooth as a table top.

At 6:20 A.M. three gun signals announced that Latham was about to start. He raced the graceful *Antoinette* down the gentle slope leading to the cliff's edge, then eased her into the air above the slate gray sea. A wireless signal to Dover brought great crowds into the streets, and they strained eyes in the direction of Calais to catch the first glimpse of an aircraft so daring as to seek to put an end to British insularity.

At first, all went well. But when Latham had completed about one-third of the distance, his engine began to misfire. Then it stopped completely. Latham had no choice but to put the craft into a simple landing glide. He set the plane down smoothly on the water's surface, without incident. The hollow wings were waterproof, and they kept the craft afloat. When the *Harpon* drew up close to take him aboard, Latham was sitting with his feet drawn up out of the water, calmly smoking a cigarette.

Latham regarded all of this as no more than a minor in convenience. He and Lavavasseur ordered a new *Antoinette* from the factory near Paris, and it arrived within a few days. Latham restarted his preparations immediately. His bad fortune, however, had not run its course.

The day after Latham's unsuccessful attempt, the *Daily Mail* received a second entry. This came from Blériot.

To Blériot, a skilled and dedicated aviator, flying was a very serious business. Swarthy and stern-looking, his face dominated by a thick, red mustache, he looked every inch a pilot. He had begun building planes in 1901, and his earliest attempts took the form of ornithopters. Besides ten years of his time, Blériot's experiments had used up $150,000. He had crashed some fifty times but had somehow managed to escape serious injury.

His present plane, dubbed the *Blériot XI*, was a small, fragile-looking monoplane. It weighed only 484 pounds and its three cylinder engine generated a mere 25 horsepower. But what the craft may have lacked in power, it made up for in ingenuity of design. Blériot's monoplane was the first with the engine in the nose, and the first to employ a tractor—not a pusher—propellor. It also featured small hinged flaps on the tips of each wing that could be moved up or down to control lateral movement.

Blériot had scored a success with the plane as recently as July 13, by virtue of a smart cross-country flight from Etampes to Orleans, a distance of 25 miles. This achievement won him $2,500, a prize posted by the Aero Club of France. During the flight Blériot had been the victim of a gasoline fire that painfully injured his left foot. When the Frenchman appeared at Les Barraques, the foot was swathed in bandages, and he had to use crutches to get around. But he was determined that the injury would not stop him. After his prize-winning flight to Orleans, Blériot had the plane crated and shipped to Calais. Ironically, it was placed aboard the same train that was transporting Latham's new *Antoinette* to Sangatte.

Bad weather prevented either Latham or Blériot from going aloft for several days. Then fate took a hand. Not long before 3 A.M. on the morning of Sunday, July 25, Blériot was roused from sleep by the racking pain in his left foot. He lay quiet for a time, listening carefully. For two days gale winds had been raging, but now it was quiet. He dressed hastily, then took his crutches and hobbled to the Cliff's edge to scan the sky and water of the Channel. There were gusting winds out of the southwest, but white, puffy clouds had replaced the low-hanging cover of recent days, giving promise of fair skies.

Blériot made his decision. He would go!

He ordered the plane to be wheeled from its shed. There was a chill in the air, and Blériot donned a pair of woollined blue overalls and a black leather jacket. He handed his crutches to a mechanic, then clambered aboard for a test flight. After circling a few times, he landed.

"Today!" he announced joyfully when the plane had rolled to a stop. "Today it will be! And we'll have no problems."

Meanwhile, there was activity at Latham's camp. Two mechanics were astir.

"The wind has died down," said one, "Shall we wake him?"

"I don't think so," said the other. "He said he would not try today."

Had the pair known of the frantic preparations now taking place at the Blériot camp, their decision would have been quite different. As it was, Latham slept on peacefully, unaware that his chance for notability and the Northcliffe prize was slipping from his grasp.

Blériot's plane was fueled and the mechanics made their final adjustments. The Frenchman then climbed to the seat between the wings and smiled and waved briefly for photographers. A mechanic spun the propellor and the engine snorted to life. At 4:35 A.M. Blériot gave the order to let go. The machine rose splendidly and headed arrow-straight for the British coast.

Later that day, Blériot told the story of the flight to a reporter for the London *Times*. These are his words:

"I could see the destroyer *Escopette* a few miles out at sea, and as she was to steam towards Dover I took my bearings from her. The destroyer was steaming at full speed, but I quickly passed her. My machine was travelling at 45 miles an hour, the revolutions of the propellers being about 1,200 to 1,400 a minute. While travelling over the Channel my monoplane was at a height of about 250 feet. At times she dipped a little, but I always got her to rise again.

"For about ten minutes after I passed the destroyer I was able by looking back to steer my course by the direction in which she was steaming. Then I lost sight of the destroyer, and the English coast was not in view, so I decided that the best thing to do was to set my steering gear for the point at which I had last seen the *Escopette* heading.

"The flight continued for about ten minutes with nothing in sight but sea and sky. It was the most anxious part of the flight, as I had no certainty that my direction was correct, but I kept my motor working at full speed and hoped that I would reach Dover all right.

"I had no fear of the machine, which was travelling beautifully. At last I sighted an outline of the land, but I was then going in the direction of Deal, and I could see the long beach very plainly. In setting my steering I had overlooked for the moment the effect of the wind, which was blowing very strong from the southwest, and had therefore deflected me eastward. I could have landed at Deal, but I had started to come to Dover, and I made up my mind to land there.

"I headed my monoplane westward, therefore, and followed the line of the coast to Dover about a mile or a little more out at sea. I could see a fleet of battleships in Dover Harbour, and I flew over these to a point where I could see my friend, M. Fontaine, with a large French tricolor, denoting the point where I was to descend. I flew in over the cliffs all right, but the descent was one of the most difficult I have ever made. When I got into the valley between the Castle and the opposite hill I found an eddying wind. I circled around twice to ease the descent, but I alighted more heavily than I had anticipated, and the monoplane was damaged."

So ended Blériot's daring performance. The time was 5:13 a.m. The first crossing of the English Channel, a 21-mile trip, had taken 38 minutes. The exact spot in Northfall Meadow when Blériot's plane came to a stop is now marked by a stone monument.

When news of the flight was received at Sangatte, Latham burst into tears. But he recovered quickly to send Blériot his felicitations. "Congratulations!" said Latham's telegram. "Hope to follow you soon."

Blériot sent back a magnanimous answer. "If you can make the flight today," he said, "we will divide the prize." But by the time Latham received the message, the wind had whipped up, making flying impossible. Latham's attempt to fly the Channel two days later ended in another failure. Not long after, out of bitter disappointment, he abandoned his career as a flier. Blériot reigned as the man of the hour. Messages of congratulations poured in from every corner of the world. The now famous monoplane was placed on exhibition and visited by 120,000 people in four days.

Blériot was involved in a humorous incident a few hours after his landing. He had just finished breakfast when three customs officers presented themselves at the hotel. After introducing themselves, they asked Blériot if he had anything to declare. He assured them that his small craft could not carry much in the way of baggage. The officers, perfectly straight-faced, then wrote out a custom ticket. It read:

"I hereby certify that I have examined Louis Blériot, master of the vessel 'Monoplane,' lately arrived from Calais, and it appears from the verbal answers of the said master to the questions put to him that there has not been on board during the voyage any infectious disease demanding the detention of the vessel, and that she is free to proceed."

Blériot's flight was cited everywhere for its far-reaching significance. Lord Northcliffe's *Daily Mail* declared that it spelled the end of security for the British people. "Locomotion is being transferred to an element where Dreadnaughts are useless and sea power no shield against attack," said the paper. "As the potentialities of the aeroplane have been proved, we must take energetic steps to develop a navy of the air."

In Berlin the *Lokal Anzeiger* observed, "England is no longer and island. Blériot flew as he liked."

And in the United States, the New York *Tribune* ran a cartoon of a bemused John Bull gazing down on a fleet of battleships in the Channel and saying, "I was never made for flying."

Almost a full year passed before the Channel was flown again. On May 23, 1910, Jacques de Lesseps, the youngest son of the famed engineer who supervised the construction of the Suez Canal, took to the air from Les Barraques and landed 37 minutes later inland from the South Foreland

Lightship. The first crossing from England to France was accomplished by the Hon. C. Rolls of "Rolls-Royce," a man who was already famous as a balloonist and auto racer. Rolls' flight was made on June 2, 1910. Instead of setting down on French soil, Rolls circled over Sangatte, dropped three envelopes containing greetings to the Aero Club of France, and then returned to England.

Soon, Channel flights became quite commonplace. Yet Louis Blériot's name continued to enthrall the public, for it had been his daring performance that had shown the way.

CHAPTER
4
ACROSS THE UNITED STATES

"We'll build a plane for you," said Orville Wright to tall Calbraith Rodgers, "and it will be the best we can do. And if the man has been born who can fly it across the United states, you are he. But the machine hasn't been built that can do it."

Wright's statement was accurate on both counts. The year was 1911. Indeed, there was no machine equal to the task of a transcontinental flight. But the man, fearless Calbraith Rodgers, surely was.

In the year 1911, a transcontinental flight was about as remote as an overnight trip to Mars. After all, the Wright brothers had achieved powered flight for the first time only seven years before. The record for "long" distance nonstop flying was held by a Curtiss pusher which, on June 13, 1910, had managed a round trip flight from New York City to Philadelphia, a distance of 149 miles. Coast to coast? It was a preposterous idea —too expensive and too perilous. To everyone but Calbraith Rodgers.

Cal believed he had a way he could solve the problem of finances; and as for danger, his family had always thrived on it. Born in Pittsburgh in 1879, Rodgers was the grand nephew of Oliver Hazard Perry, hero of the battle of Lake Erie in the War of 1812, and the great grandson of Matthew Calbraith Perry, the United States Navy commodore who helped to open Japan to the West in 1855. Rodgers' father was an Army captain who had died fighting the Indians in the Southwest.

A service career was planned for Cal, but in childhood he suffered an attack of scarlet fever that impaired his hearing. Years later the impairment caused him to be rejected by the U.S. Naval Academy.

Six feet, four inches tall and weighing 200 pounds, Cal was a daring young man who got his thrills playing football while in college, and later as an amateur road racer. He had married, but was too restless to settle down.

Aviation pioneering—that seemed to be the ticket. In June 1911, he traveled to Dayton to attend the Wright Brothers' school for prospective aviators. He soloed the first day and within a week Orville was describing him as "the third best aviator who'd ever flown."

He impressed the Wrights to such an extent that they offered him the opportunity to pilot one of their machines in an endurance meet in Chicago. In the nine days of competition, Cal spent a total of 28 hours in the air, good enough to win the championship and almost $12,000 in prize money.

An attempt at a coast-to-coast flight was a logical next step. The Wrights would build the plane. Cal would fly it. But where was the money to finance the trip to come from?

Cal's cousin, John Rodgers, a U.S. Navy pilot, had the answer. J. Ogden Armour, the wealthy meat packer, was about to introduce a new soft drink, carbonated and grape-flavored, it was called *Vin Fiz*. Why not tie-in with Armour? It was a brilliant piece of strategy. Armour supplied a special four-car train for the trip that included Pullman quarters for Cal, his wife and the plane's maintenance crew, a dining car, a hangar-car equipped to make repairs and a storage car that carried spare parts, medical supplies (to treat Cal's injuries which were considered inevitable), tools, oil, gasoline and a Palmer-Singer sports car to pick Cal up when he landed the plane following each day's hop. Rodgers was to follow the train across the country using it as a base of operations. Long white streamers were strung from the roofs of the cars to make the train easy to recognize. Cal was to receive five dollars for every mile flown in the heavily populated East, and four dollars for every mile covered in the West.

Rodgers, in turn, agreed to carry and drop circulars advertising *Vin Fiz* and to fly to towns off his route to allow Armour's publicity people, who were also to be berthed in the train, to promote the drink more widely. Rodgers also agreed to name the plane the *Vin Fiz*, and permit the two words to be blazoned on the fuselage. He was, in effect, the world's first flying advertisement.

It took two months for the Wrights to build Cal's biplane. It did not look far advanced from the machine they flew at Kitty Hawk. The wings resembled a pair of long box kites laid horizontally. The body was 21 feet in length made of slim spruce struts that were trussed with steel wire. The watercooled engine developed 28 horsepower. The gas tank held fifteen gallons, enough to keep the craft aloft for three and one-half hours. It was capable of generating 62 mph, if there were no headwind.

To fly the rig, Cal had to cram his body into a seat mounted near the front of the fuselage, and use both hands and feet. There was no cockpit; he was exposed to the weather.

The Wrights lent Cal their chief mechanic, Charlie Taylor. "Oh, God," said Orville to Cal, "you will need him . . ." Accommodations were provided for him in the special train.

Despite the fragile nature of the plane, Cal developed a deep affection for it. Although its official name was *Vin Fiz*, he preferred to call it Betsy. He would pat it and talk to it as one might treat a pet horse.

The *Vin Fiz* had no navigational instruments, not even a compass. Cal had no charts of the terrain he was to cross, and it was not a time of weather forecasts. He had no defense against tricky gusts of wind or stiff turbulence; no way to guard against the perils of sudden rain squalls, heavy fogs or pasture fences and ditches. What he did have was his boundless confidence and his bulldog courage.

Rodgers planned to start the trip within sight of the Atlantic. He had the *Vin Fiz* shipped to Sheepshead Bay, not far from Coney Island in Brooklyn. Late in the afternoon of September 17, 1911, he stuffed his lanky frame into the pilot's seat. He wore his usual flying garb: a cloth cap and goggles, a business suit, a white shirt and tie, a leather jacket and long leather leggings. He smoked a long cigar. He waved jauntily to the crowd, and then yelled out, "O.K! Start her up, Charlie!"

Mechanic Charlie Taylor spun one prop; his assistant spun the other. Three men held the plane until the engine had developed a prodigious clatter. On a signal from Cal, they released their grip, and the *Vin Fiz* crept forward on its bicycle wheels. Gathering speed, it bounded into the air and gained altitude gracefully. At two thousand feet, Cal circled the field and waved to the awed crowd.

He circled again and then headed west. New York City's landmark passed below—the Brooklyn Bridge, the elevated railroad structures and the Metropolitan Life Tower. He followed Broadway north to 23rd Street and then crossed the Hudson River to Hoboken, New Jersey. In the vast railroad marshalling yards, he spotted his train. Plans called for him to meet the train later in Middletown, New York, about one hundred miles to the north. So Cal would not become confused by the great maze of tracks leading out of Hoboken, every half mile on the line he was to follow was marked by a large square of white canvas—a veritable dotted line across the face of New Jersey.

It was simple. Two hours later Cal saw the spires of Middletown. A crowd of nine thousand had assembled at the fairgrounds, and Cal brought the *Vin Fiz* down smartly amidst rousing cheers.

There was jubilation aboard the train that night. Cal had made a total of 104 miles in 105 minutes, and the *Vin Fiz* had consumed only 7.5 gallons of fuel. That meant that Cal could do 250, even 350 miles without refueling. In his bliss, Cal wired the New York *Times:* "No man ever had a truer machine and a more perfect engine. It's Chicago in four days if everything goes all right."

Before take off the next morning, Charlie Taylor told Cal that he didn't believe that the *Vin Fiz* could clear the trees at the end of the fairgrounds. "Let's move it to a bigger field," he urged. But Cal scoffed at the idea. He was so confident he didn't even bother to strap himself into his seat. "Let 'er go, Charlie," he called out. The *Vin Fiz* lumbered down the take off strip and into the air.

Miraculously, Cal cleared the trees and he was chortling to himself when suddenly a string of power lines loomed ahead. Cal recalled how a friend of his had hit power lines in Chicago—and had died as a result. He cut the engine. The *Vin Fiz* fell straight downward into a chicken coop, sustaining severe damage. Since he wasn't strapped in, Cal was thrown clear, and managed to escape with a bump on the head.

It took Charlie Taylor and his crew three days to make the *Vin Fiz* airworthy again. The next time he tried, Cal got the ship into the air without difficulty, but a leaky radiator and a faulty cylinder forced him down in a potato field at Hancock, New York, 96 miles to the west. A crowd of curious townspeople, eager to see a flying machine, tramped across the field, ruining the farmer's potatoes. He made Cal reimburse him for the loss.

The next morning Cal took off for Binghamton. Anxious to make up for lost time, he left the railroad tracks to take a more direct route across a mountain ridge. It was a sad mistake. When he set the plane down, he was told that he had landed on the outskirts of Scranton, Pennsylvania. Binghamton was seventy miles to the north.

Whenever Cal landed, crowds hailed his arrival and Scranton was no exception. Yet his well wishers were one of Cal's greatest hazards, for they often attempted to strip the *Vin Fiz* clean in their quest for souvenirs. The police came to his rescue at Scranton, and gave him directions to Binghamton where his train awaited him. He left Binghamton that afternoon to fly on to Elmira where a holiday had been declared in his honor. Schools and factories were closed down and virtually all of the town's residents was on hand to greet him.

The *Vin Fiz* limped across western New York State ever so slowly. There were times Cal must have wondered if he was ever going to see Ohio, much less California. He ripped a hole in the elevator taking off from Elmira. A faulty magneto forced him down in Canisteo. A slipped plug caused another emergency landing near Olean. Taking off, the *Vin Fiz* struck a pair of barbed wire fences "and was shredded like a cabbage," according to one account. Cal escaped, but the plane had to be hauled to Salamanca, New York, for repairs.

Then the *Vin Fiz* skipped across Ohio without a hitch. But Indiana was a different story. In Huntington, 3,500 people inspected the plane, and almost all of them wrote their names on her. One person went so far as to etch his name into the veneer of the propeller. The prop had to be reglued before take off. Other delays and misadventures plagued the flight, but the worst happened in Hammond where high winds kept the plane on the ground for four days.

When Cal arrived in Chicago, he announced to newsmen that he planned to keep going. "I'm going to be the first man to cross the continent by air," he pledged. "I don't care how long it takes me."

Leaving Chicago, Cal became lost in the labyrinth of railroad tracks, and it took him more than a hour to make Lockport, 38 miles away. The next day he got as far as Springfield. Cal arrived in Marshall, Missouri, on October 10. When he landed in Marshall, his flight reached the 1,998-mile mark, breaking the record of 1,925 miles held by Harry Atwood.

Cal regarded Kansas City as the halfway mark, and was thrilled when he arrived there the next day. A huge throng jammed Overland Park where he was scheduled to land. Out of gratitude, Cal put the *Vin Fiz* through dives, sharp banks and figure eights. The crowd loved it.

Cal left Kansas City on October 15; Fort Worth, Texas, was his destination. Over Venita, Oklahoma, he ran into a ferocious storm. Lightning filled the black sky; thunder boomed. Rain and wind almost beat the spindly plane to the ground. Soaking wet, Cal wrestled the controls in a desperate effort to keep from cracking up. His eyes burned; his head throbbed. Every muscle in his body ached. It was the most frightening part of the trip. After a night's rest, Cal was in the air again. A leaky oil tank and a cracked cylinder brought him down in McAlester, Oklahoma.

Fort Worth was now 191 miles away, but Cal traveled more than 300 miles to get there. Leaving McAlester, he followed the Katy Railroad, but mistook a spur for the main track. Stationmasters realized that he was off course and built signal fires to bring him down. It worked. Cal landed at Bonita, Texas, and got proper directions.

Four thousand people were waiting when Cal landed at Fort Worth, and there were big crowds at Dallas and Waco, too. Their enthusiasm never failed to lift his spirits, and he invariably responded by performing dizzying stunts which could easily have killed him.

When flying from Fort Worth to Dallas, Cal encountered a new and deadly hazard—an insolent eagle. The bird raced the *Vin Fiz* for a good distance, then suddenly wheeled and shot for the plane like a dive bomber. Cal braced himself for the collision. But at the last second the eagle veered off, probably frightened away by the engine's bluster.

Texas was full of perils and Cal spent two weeks there. While the *Vin Fiz* was on the ground in Fort Worth, vandals tore off a wing. The plane was windbound for a day at Kyle and later for a day at Sanderson. The machine hit a hillock on taking off at Spofford and had to be held over for repairs. Cal himself barely escaped serious injury at El Paso. Coming in for his landing, a gas pump connection suddenly sheared off, stalling the engine. The *Vin Fiz* plunged to earth. Cal was struck on the head by the loosened gas tank and knocked unconscious. He made a quick recovery, however, and managed to attend a bullfight across the border in Mexico while the *Vin Fiz* was being repaired.

On the last day of October, Cal managed to make Willcox, Arizona. The next day he moved on to Tucson. Most people in the Southwest had never seen an airplane before, and the *Vin Fiz* drew mammoth crowds. In Phoenix the crowd was so large, Cal could not land at the appointed field. He set down at another spot, refueled and took off again before the crowd could catch up.

Over the desert, Cal had another encounter with an eagle. This one dove at the *Vin Fiz* several times, and on each pass raked the plane with its beak or claws, tearing holes in the filmy fabric that covered the wings and fuselage. Fearing the plane would soon be sent into a death-dealing dive, Cal gunned the motor and headed down in search of a landing place. This strategy saved the day. When Cal put the nose down, the huge bird, apparently believing it had overcome its adversary, flew off in triumph.

All was going well as the *Vin Fiz* crossed the state border into California. The next stop was to be Banning. Then, with the goal within grasp, the gallant adventure almost came to a tragic end. Over the Salton Sea, the No. 1 cylinder exploded. The loud report almost split Cal's eardrums. The plane lurched crazily. Metal splinters filled the air, many of them penetrating Cal's right arm, the arm used to control the warping lever. Cal was never more courageous. Wracked with pain and with his arm gushing blood, he put the plane into a series of wide spirals and landed gracefully beside a tiny railroad station. It took doctors two hours to remove the splinters and bandage him.

Cal's engine was beyond repair, however. He persuaded the mechanics to install the "old" engine, the one that he had used in the Chicago endurance meet, and long since regarded as worn out.

So equipped, Cal next had to negotiate one of the most crucial tests of the entire journey, the tortuous San Gorgonio Pass. Here swift winds swirl through a narrow mountain gap, where sheer rock walls on each side rise six thousand feet.

Although there was scarcely any leeway, Cal plunged the *Vin Fiz* into the notch without blinking an eye. He was about halfway through the pass when everything seemed to go wrong. A connecting rod snapped and the radiator started gushing steam and hot water. Cal knew his life was at stake. He searched desperately for a place to land. The canyon walls rose on each side; directly below was jutting rock. The *Vin Fiz* lunged forward drunkenly. Then ahead, beyond the canyon, Cal spotted a plowed field. Targeting on it, Cal put the *Vin Fiz* into a harrowing dive. At the last minute, he pulled out and flung the machine to the ground. Cal sat dazed; it was several minutes before he could move.

The engine required major repairs but there were no replacement parts left. What the *Vin Fiz* really needed was a whole new motor, but it would take the better part of a week for one to arrive. Cal could not wait; victory was too near. Back up into the air he went.

Late in the afternoon of November 5, Cal at long last reached his destination, A crowd of 20,000 at Tournament Park in Pasadena went wild with excitement when they saw the *Vin Fiz* come out of the east. Cal himself became caught up in the hysteria. He did a series of corkscrew banks and hair-raising turns. Five times he circled above his screaming fans. A white sheet had been spread out on the ground as a target, and, when he had completed his acrobatics, Cal brought the *Vin Fiz* down within twenty-five feet of it.

The crowd mobbed him. They carried him on their shoulders to an open touring car, and an American flag was draped over his shoulders. Then the car circled the park, with thousands of spectators chasing after it. It was a wild melee. But it was not just Pasadena that hailed Cal and the *Vin Fiz;* the whole nation cheered his effort.

Statistically, Cal had flown 4,251 miles in 49 days. It had taken 68 separate flights. His actual flying time was three days, ten hours and fourteen minutes. He had crash-landed nine times. The *Vin Fiz* arrived in California with only two parts of the original plane intact—the vertical rudder and the drip pan.

It was a costly undertaking for everyone. Armour's expenses were estimated to be $180,000 for parts, the special train and general promotion. Although Cal earned about $20,000 under the $4 and $5 per mile agreement, he had to pay out more than $17,000 for repairs, and the *Vin Fiz* cost him $5,000 originally. But Cal hadn't made the flight for what he could earn. "Never mind about the money," he said. "I did it, didn't I?"

A few days after the glorious finish at Pasadena, Cal made arrangements to fly the *Vin Fiz* to Long Beach where he was to wet the plane's skids in the Pacific. He never made it. En route the engine failed for the last time and the *Vin Fiz* plummeted to earth once again. Cal's body was dragged from the wreckage and at first rescuers thought that he was dead. But Cal's luck was still running strong. He spent a month in the hospital and then, with a new plane, was back flying again.

Cal became a well known figure in Long Beach. He took tourists for rides—for fancy fees—and gave flying exhibitions. On April 2, 1912, he was testing his machine just offshore when he encountered a flight of seagulls. They flew into the plane and through it, swatting Cal on the face and shoulders. Momentarily stunned, Cal lost control and the machine dropped like a stone from a tall building. It crashed in about four feet of water. A pair of lifeguards were the first to reach it. Cal's neck and back were broken. Death was instantaneous, doctors said.

Almost as tragic as Cal's death was the quickness with which his life and epic flight were forgotten. Perhaps it was because of the avowed commercialism of the venture. Newspapers of the day all but ignored it, at least until the crossing had reached its final stages. Or perhaps Cal lived too briefly to exploit the experience.

Whatever the reason, the name Calbraith Rodgers is little remembered. Yet he left a legacy of thrilling memories, and the daring triumph should rightly be ranked as a landmark event in man's conquest of the air.

CHAPTER
5
ACROSS
THE
ATLANTIC

When World War I ended in November 1918, pilots in both England and the United States turned their attention to a transatlantic flight. The idea obsessed them. By the following spring, several groups of airmen had completed the planning and enlisted the financial backing necessary to such a venture. By May, the situation was tense. The year 1919 has come to be known as the year of the "great transatlantic race." This chapter tells that story.

The first attempt to cross the Atlantic dates as far back as 1910. On October 15 of that year, one Walter Wellman, an American explorer, and five companions, embarked from Atlantic City in an airship named the *America*. Its two engines enabled the craft to lumber along at twenty miles an hour. It was an ambitious undertaking, for no airship up to that time had even managed a voyage of more than nine hundred miles. Wellman was not to threaten the record. Not long after the trip began, the airship suffered an engine breakdown, and then was struck by strong winds from the north. By the end of the second day, Wellman's goal was no longer Europe. He would have gladly settled for Bermuda or even Florida's eastern shore. Mechanical difficulties continued to plague the voyage, and on the third day Wellman and his colleagues abandoned the airship in favor of a lifeboat they were carrying. Soon after, they were picked up by a passing ship. The

America drifted away and was never seen again. So ended the first attempt at an Atlantic air crossing.

As aircraft became more airworthy and engines more powerful, people began to realize that the airplane, not the airship, offered the most likely means of spanning the Atlantic. Enter Lord Northcliffe—again! On April 1, 1913, his newspaper, the London *Daily Mail*, offered a prize of 10,000 pounds for the first transatlantic flight. Naturally this immediately excited wide interest in the project. Northcliffe set certain conditions. The flight had to be made from any point in the British Isles to any point in the United States or Canada, or in the opposite direction. It had to be completed within seventy-two consecutive hours. Aircraft could not be changed during the flight. And the flight had to be direct, that is, it could not be made in parts, by island hopping by way of the Azores, for instance.

Every airman of the day knew what these rules meant in practical terms. It would have to be, first of all, a west-to-east flight, in order to take advantage of the prevailing winds. A glance at the North Atlantic region of a globe showed the shortest route—from St. John's in Newfoundland to the southeastern coast of Ireland, a distance of just two-thousand miles. Talk about flying the Atlantic was abruptly ended in August 1914 with the outbreak of World War I.

Aviation made great strides on both sides of the Atlantic during the war. In 1917, the year that the United States entered the conflict, an Army flyer made the statement that "not a single air officer in Washington has ever seen a fighting plane." The U.S. had fewer than 250 aircraft at the time, and none was combat-worthy by European standards. But by the war's end, the U.S. had forty-five air squadrons at the fighting fronts in Europe, and the whole air service, Army, Navy and Marines, numbered 20,000 officers and 170,000 men, Similarly, tremendous strides had been made in the technical development of aircraft.

Despite the advances, the Atlantic was still a stern challenge. Weather was a critical problem. The Atlantic is so vast that it is hardly ever completely free of clouds, fog and storms. But a pilot of the post-World War I era never expected to be told where rough weather lay over an entire transatlantic route. The reporting facilities simply did not exist. Even if such information were available, his plane would be in the air so long there would be ample time for the weather to change. The enormous amount of fuel required for crossing the Atlantic in one "leap" was another obstacle. No one really knew whether engines existed that could carry that weight and still function dependably for hours on end. It was still a mission filled with extraordinary risks.

Most people of the day believed that the first man to fly the Atlantic would be British. There was enormous activity on the English side of the Atlantic, with no fewer than seven planes being readied for the ocean crossing. The ranks thinned quickly, however. Three planes crashed during test flights, and a fourth could not get off the ground when fully loaded. That left three teams: Harry Hawker and K. Mackenzie-Grieve, Fred Raynham and Bill Morgan, and Jack Alcock and Arthur Brown.

Harry Hawker was a particular favorite. The twenty-seven year old son of an Australian blacksmith, Hawker was regarded as one of Europe's most skilled fliers. He was chief pilot for Sopwith Aviation Company, whose World War I "Camels" and "Pups" had made Sopwith a household name. When the war ended the company made up its mind to become established in commercial aviation. They planned to declare this policy to the whole world by building a transatlantic plane. Would Hawker fly it? Indeed. Mackenzie-Grieve was named navigator.

Sopwith's designers conceived a small two-passenger biplane, light and swift, with a single Rolls Royce engine of 350 horsepower. It had two notable innovations. One was a landing gear that was detachable. As soon as the plane was airborne, this could be dropped, adding about seven miles an hour to the plane's speed. The other was a small boat which was built bottom-side-up into the fuselage just aft of the cockpit. It could be easily sprung free in case of a forcedown at sea. The plane was named the *Atlantic*.

Late in March, Hawker, Grieve and a covey of mechanics booked passage on the freighter *Digby* bound for St. John's, Newfoundland. The *Atlantic* was disassembled, packed carefully into crates, and stowed aboard. The plan was to take off from St. John's on the evening of April 16, when the moon would be full. If all went well, they would be in Ireland the following afternoon.

Hawker had a competitor close at his heels in the person of Fred Raynham, a veteran British airman. Raynham was chief test pilot for Martinsyde, another aircraft manufacturer, and that company had provided him with a deep-bellied, single engine bomber, and like the *Atlantic*, a biplane. The Raynham contingent arrived in Newfoundland ten days after Hawker's men.

Newfoundland, its terrain and its weather, were a sad jolt to the British pilots. It is doubtful whether they did much investigating of conditions before their departure from England. Newfoundland is a land of rocky, barren hills, broken by marshes and thick forests. Flat and open fields are almost as rare as trout streams in the Sahara, and what level land does exist is used for farming. Winters are long and cold, summers are short, and the brief spring is a period of damp and foggy weather.

The realization that Newfoundland was less than ideal hit Hawker quickly. The harbor at St. John's was choked with ice when the *Digby* arrived. Hawker and his party and their precious crates had to disembark at Placentia Bay, then make their way to St. John's by rail. Hawker found the city covered with snow and more threatening. The roads were deep with mud. He finally found a field where the *Atlantic* could be assembled and tested, but it was far from what he had in mind originally. Hawker's plane required 500-yards of runway to get off the ground. This field gave him more than the 500-yards needed, but in an L shape. One leg of the L was 200 yards in length, the other 400 yards. He hired some men to pull out the stumps and fill the ruts—and said a few prayers.

The field was located at Mount Pearl, about six miles from St. John's but it took almost two weeks before Hawker could get the heavy crates to the site. Time after time, the lumbering wagons bogged down in the thick muck. Raynham's problems were not quite so serious, for a representative from Martinsyde had come to St. John's in January and found a field much closer to town.

There was good-natured rivalry between the two camps and members of the two teams visited back and forth. The two pilots entered into a gentleman's agreement that each would give the other two-hour notice of his plans to take off.

Both got their machines assembled. Both ran successful tests. Then they waited for clear skies—and waited and waited. The sun was almost never seen. Usually it rained. Day after day passed. April gave way to May. A newspaperman told Hawker jokingly that he could not expect to take off before June. Hawker felt the statement might be closer to fact than fiction.

In the United States, meanwhile, the Navy was making what must be described as a ponderous effort to cross the sea by air. During the war, German U boats had all but taken over the Atlantic. Navy Department officials agreed that the only way to end the submarine menace was from the air. Late in 1917, the Navy awarded the Curtiss Company a contract to build four huge "flying boats."

Glenn Curtiss, whose contribution to the development of aviation in the United States rivals that of the Wrights, had long favored the building of planes that were usable at sea. In 1914, Curtiss had built a monstrous flying boat called the *America*. It had a wing spread of seventy-two feet and was powered by three engines, each rated at 160 horsepower. World War I prevented the plane from making an attempt at a transatlantic crossing. The ship was sold to the British and was used successfully on anti-submarine patrol duty.

Curtiss had the first of the Navy's flying boats completed late in 1918. It was test flown in October of that year, and early the following month it made a successful flight to Washington. On November 11, the war ended. Interest in the flying boat project promptly died, at least for a time.

There were many people who had faith in the giant planes and believed that they were capable of significant accomplishments. One of these men was Commander John Towers, one of the Navy's first pilots.

He was a close friend of Curtiss and had agreed to co-pilot the *America* across the Atlantic. He had never given up hope that some day the flight could be made and if a Navy plane should be the one to do it, so much the better. When the war ended, he began stirring up interest in the project. One man that he contacted was Franklin D. Roosevelt, then Assistant Secretary of the Navy. "If it were up to me, I'd tell you to go ahead tomorrow," Roosevelt told Towers. "But I'm not the Secretary; it's up to Joe Daniels." Roosevelt became so enthusiastic that eventually he enlisted Secretary Daniels' support. Approval for the flight was granted early in 1919.

A word about the planes. They were huge, the biggest heavier-than-air ships ever built up to that time. They were of biplane design, and each had a wingspan of 126 feet and a length of 68 feet. The tail structure was unique. In conventional flying boats, the tail was attached to the hull. But in Curtiss planes, the tail was held in place by booms stretching out from the hull. This made for less weight.

The hull itself was divided into separate compartments. The navigator's compartment was in the bow. Behind it came the section where the pilots sat; there were two of them, each with a set of controls. In the stern was the radioman's cabin. Two sections held fuel tanks. The crew also included two machinist mates—a total of six men. When fully loaded, each plane weighed more than twelve tons. The Navy christened them "NC's"—N for Navy, C for Curtiss. But they were known derisively as "Nancies."

To lift the tremendous weight, each plane was fitted out with four four-hundred horsepower Liberty engines. Two were mounted on the wings, and the other two fixed on top of the hull in tandem. Three of the engines had tractor propellors, while the rear center engine had a pusher propellor.

The NC's could achieve speeds of ninety-three miles an hour, excellent for ships so big. However, they had a range of only 1,300 miles. The shortest route across the Atlantic—from Newfoundland to Ireland—is close to 2,000 miles. Thus the Navy decided to break the trip into two parts. The first hop would be from Rockaway, New York, where the planes were based, to Trepassey Bay in Newfoundland. From Trepassey, the plan was to head to the Azores, a distance of about 1,200 miles, and the longest leg of the journey. Then from the Azores, the planes were to fly to Lisbon, Portugal, and finally on to Plymouth, the port from which the *Mayflower* had sailed some three hundred years before.

May was set as the month for the flight because the sea would be calm enough then to permit emergency landings. As a further precaution, Navy destroyers were to be spaced every fifty miles along the over-the-sea portion of the flight. This meant that no plane was ever to be more than 25 miles from a surface ship and always within radio range. Obviously, the Navy was taking few chances. Officials also planned to send a complete set of spare parts for each plane ahead to Trepassey Bay in the event repairs were needed for the transatlantic portion of the flight.

Through the early months of 1919, the Navy groomed the four NC's at the air station at Rockaway, a sandy spit of land south of the western tip of long Island. Things seldom went smoothly. Gale force winds damaged the NC-1. The NC-2 had greater misfortune. One February day the plane was skimming across Jamaica Bay for a take off when a smaller Navy plane, which was engaged in depth charge practice, dropped one of its explosive charges about 150-feet from the flying boat. No one was injured but the plane had to be scrapped, leaving only three to make the crossing attempt. Early in May a hangar fire damaged the re-built NC-1 and the NC-4. Weather was another problem. May one was set as the day of departure, but on that date furious storms rose up to lash the East Coast, and they lasted for days.

On the morning of Thursday, May 8, 1919, the Navy decided the time had come. Reports from ships at sea and Coast Guard installations along the Eastern seaboard told of clearing skies. Commander Towers, who had been named to organize and command the flight, gave the orders to the crews to "Board your planes." Two planes were taken from their enormous hangar; a third had spent the night on the beach. Then one by one they were rolled onto a rail system that led to the water. The engines were started, and the three taxied to the more placid waters of nearby Jamaica Bay. Then they turned into the wind and lifted into the air.

Columbus may have had less travail crossing the Atlantic than the NC's. They were plagued by woes from the very beginning. The first to suffer was the NC-4. The plane was not more than three hundred miles out of Rockaway when an engine went out. Shortly after, a second engine broke down, and the plane had to land at sea. It managed to chug its way to a naval air station at Chatham, on Cape Cod, Massachusetts, where repairs were made. Meanwhile, the other two planes made it safely to Halifax, Nova Scotia, and after some minor difficulties proceeded to Trepassey Bay. There they were delayed by bad weather, giving NC-4 a chance to catch up.

Even when the weather did clear, the pilots of NC-1 and NC-4 could not get their ships into the air. They would roar across the bay, but simply could not lift out of the water. This thoroughly amused the British pilots. "Why don't you just sail the Atlantic," Hawker said to one of the crews. "Your planes look like they could make it that way." Mechanics on Towers' plane, the NC-3, drained off about 200-pounds of gasoline. Still the ship remained glued to the bay on its take off run. Then Towers ordered the long range radio ripped out, a saving of seventy pounds, and then he cut one of the engineers out of the crew. The man weighed 160 pounds. At last the plane took to the air, but just barely.

The three ships left Trepassey Bay late in the afternoon of May 16, so as to make most of the flight to the Azores at night, arriving at the small cluster of islands at daybreak. Clear weather had been forecast. Their goal was Ponta Delgada, on São Miguel Island, the capital, where Navy personnel awaited. Horta, on the island of Fayal, 200 miles west of Ponta Delgada, was designated as an emergency stop. Fuel, spare parts, and even complete engines were available there.

The planes planned to fly in formation with Towers' ship leading the way. During the night, NC-3 and NC-4 came close to colliding. Towers ordered the planes to break formation and put each pilot on his own. Through the night and into the next morning, the planes droned on. The dull routine was broken at mid-morning when fog was sighted and rain began. The forecast of clear weather had been dreadfully wrong.

To get out of the weather, the planes climbed to 4000 feet. The winds grew more turbulent, and both NC-1 and NC-3, which trailed NC-4, were given a frightful buffeting. With their crude instruments, the pilots could not tell if they were flying on a level course or whether one wing was pointing toward the boiling sea and the other skyward. The compass needles bounced crazily in the rough air. Worst of all, both planes were unable to get a bearing from the ships of the destroyer chain below. The two became hopelessly lost.

Lieutenant Commander P. N. L. (Pat) Bellinger, in command of the NC-1, knew that his plane was near the Azores, and that mountain peaks there reached 7,000 feet. Not knowing his position, he was afraid of ramming into a "stuffed cloud." He told his pilot, "If this fog doesn't lift in a few minutes, we'll have to land." The fog did not clear. "Put her down," Bellinger ordered. The sea was raging. As the NC-1 glided down, a mountainous wave buried her. Bellinger heard the snap of struts and loud crunches from the hull. He knew the NC-1 would not fly again.

Not many miles away, Commander Jack Towers was about to make the same decision. His navigator's calculations showed that the NC-3 was off course to the south. Fuel was running low. The pilots were exhausted from battling the controls in the heavy turbulence. The navigator suggested that they land in order to contact some of the destroyers and take radio compass bearings. Towers agreed. "Let's go down and take a look," he said to his pilot, Holden C. (Dick) Richardson. When the plane had reached five hundred feet, Towers asked, "How's it look?" Richardson peered down. "No problem, Commander," he answered.

But Richardson had not seen the sea. The fog had settled on the surface, obscuring the water. Unknown to Richardson, waves of up to sixty feet in height heaved below. "O.K.," said Towers, "You're driving; set her down whenever you're ready." The giant bird glided down, struck the crest of one wave, and slammed into a second. Struts sprung and control wires slackened. The hull sprung a leak and water gushed in. Everyone on board knew—the NC-3 was out of the race.

The NC-4 had better fortune. Like the other skippers, Lieutenant Commander A. C. (Putty) Read had seen the weather turn. But Read was determined to stay in visual contact with the destroyers as long as he possibly could, and he did not order his plane aloft and out of the low cover. The NC-4 ran into fog patches but, Read had occasional glimpses of the sea. The NC-4 passed over destroyer No. 16, the *Hopewell.* The fog thickened. Read radioed ahead to the next destroyer in the chain, the *Stockton,* and asked for a report on the weather. "No visibility," answered the ship. Read figured that at his present speed he would be over the *Stockton* in fifty minutes. "We're going up," he radioed the ship "We'll look for you later."

When the NC-4 reached the *Stockton,* the fog was so thick that Read decided not to descend. He radioed for weather information. Destroyer No. 19, the *Dent,* answered that visibility was zero. No. 20, the *Philip,* reported "Heavy mist." But destroyer No. 21, the *Waters,* the last ship before land fall, reported "Visibility ten miles."

This is what Read had hoped to hear. The NC-4 flew on, unaware that the NC-1 and NC-3 had made emergency landings and that their crews were fighting for survival. Hour after hour passed. Read was almost certain the plane had been blown off course. Their gas was running low. He knew he would have to put down soon. The plane was at 3,400 feet between two banks of clouds. The one above was pudding-thick. The one below churned constantly.

Read stared down at the swirling mass. Then, for just an instant, the cloud parted. Read's heart leapt at what he saw—broken water caused by a meeting of cross currents. The rip meant that land was near.

He ordered the plane into a quick descent. The rifts in the fog were more frequent now. Read saw some rock formations jutting out of the ocean, and then the shoreline of an island, a big one. Read was ecstatic. He realized that even if the plane should be forced down, they would be safe.

The fog had lifted. Visibility was ten or twelve miles. "How's the fuel," Read asked his engineer. "Plenty," came the answer. "We can make three hundred miles." Read grinned. He set a course directly for Ponta Delgada, without stopping at Horta. The NC-4 passed over destroyer No. 22. Then the fog grew thick again. The plane got off course. It was too hazardous to go on, Read decided. He ordered the pilot to return to Horta. They landed in the wrong bay, took off and landed again. This time they were "right on Horta's front porch."

The crew of the NC-4 soon learned what had happened to the other planes. The men of the NC-1 had been picked up by a Greek ship, then transferred to the destroyer *Gridley*. The floating plane was judged a hazard to navigation. The *Gridley* rammed the wreckage, sending it to the bottom.

The crew of the NC-3 sailed the downed craft almost as if it were a ship. For a full day and a part of another, they limped toward Ponta Delgada. They were not sighted until they were seven miles from land.

"Good God," said Read when he heard the news. "Is everybody all right?"

"Not even an injury," he was told.

"And what about the plane," he asked.

"She's a wreck, a total wreck," came the answer.

Read turned to his crew. "Well," he said, "I guess it's up to us."

When the NC-1 and NC-3 had landed at Halifax, and the seriousness of the United States challenge thus became widely known, the dramatic race began to take shape in the public mind. It must be said that the sentiment of most people was with the British fliers. Their planes were tiny compared to the mammoth flying boats of the Americans, and they were competing as individuals, without the support of their government. The American airmen, on the other hand, had the goods and services of a mighty navy at their disposal. Even in America, some people rooted for the British.

Despite the Americans' success in reaching Nova Scotia, Hawker and Grieve were unworried. They knew that their greater speed and shorter route would enable them to overtake the NC's even if the American planes built up a long lead. Then word reached the British airmen that Read had landed in the Azores and was planning to continue his flight within a matter of hours. This news changed the situation. Hawker and Grieve knew that they could delay no longer. National honor was at stake.

The weather on May 18 was not favorable. A twenty mile-an-hour crosswind raked one leg of the field, making the take off a delicate business. But Hawker would not wait. He notified Raynham he was leaving, then ordered the *Atlantic* filled with fuel, a 350-gallon load. The heavily laden plane moved clumsily across the field, then lifted uncertainly into the air, barely missing a low fence at the end of its run. Hawker put the ship into a steady climb, and as he circled toward the ocean, he released the landing gear. He felt the plane leap forward. Just before he reached the sea, he passed over Raynham's camp where the crew was busily fueling the Martinsyde ship. He waggled his plane's wings in salute and then headed out over the gray ocean.

An hour later, Raynham was ready. The ground was soft, and on his first attempt he could not get up speed enough to lift off. He cut the engine just before he reached the end of the field. A second try produced the same results. On his third attempt, the Martinsyde lumbered from the muddy turf only to be stung by a vicious gust that slammed the heavy plane back to earth. Onlookers pulled Raynham from the wreckage. He suffered only bruises but his navigator injured an eye. There was not the slightest chance of repairing the ship. Britain's hopes now rested solely on Harry Hawker.

After leaving the coastline, Harry climbed to 10,000-feet to get above the fog. The motor thundered faultlessly. The stars were bright. The air speed indicator showed that they were making 105 miles an hour. Hawker turned and smiled at Grieve. It seemed easy.

They were about four hours out when Harry thought he saw "pretty heavy stuff" ahead. He was right. Shortly after, they were in it. These were rain squalls from the north and they slapped at the plane, tossing it about. Hawker and Grieve had been through worse. So long as they remained aloft, with plenty of space between their ship and the water, there was no cause for great alarm. Then Grieve discovered that their radio had gone dead. They were cut off from the world. Still Hawker was confident. The radio he regarded as a convenience, not a necessity. However, trouble of a more serious nature was beginning to build.

Hawker made a routine instrument check. What he saw sent a shiver down his spine. The thermometer showed the water temperature in the radiator to be 176 degrees, eight degrees above normal. He opened the shutters on the radiator to admit the chill night air. Nothing happened. The temperature continued to rise. Hawker believed that the filter was clogged with particles of rust. This had happened to him before. Sometimes a dive dislodged the rust. Hawker took the plane to 12,000-feet, then cut the engine and nosed the plane over. He allowed the ship to plunge downward for half-a-mile before pulling out. It seemed to do the trick. However, within an hour the temperature had climbed up again. Hawker tried a second dive. It worked, but not so effectively as the first one.

Hawker kept his eyes glued to the temperature gauge. It would be disastrous if the temperature reached the boiling point and stayed there very long. The water would boil away as steam, and then the engine would burn itself out. To reduce the engine's heating, Hawker throttled down the plane's speed and limited its altitude to 12,000-feet. Fortunately, the storms had subsided. Grieve took star sightings that showed them to be on course. Hawker handled the controls with extra caution to conserve the engine's water. "We still might make it," he thought.

Gray dawn was beginning to show. But no sun came, only a great bank of clouds with black thunderheads that reached 15,000 feet. Hawker put the plane into a steep climb to try to get above them. Steam spewed from the radiator and coated the upper wing with a thin film of ice. Certain tragedy loomed. Hawker had no choice but to shut off the engine and put he ship into a glide. At one thousand feet, he opened the throttle. Nothing; not a sound. The engine would not respond. Grieve desperately pumped gas into the engine with the hand pump. The raging sea was fearfully near. "I'm going to put her down," Hawker yelled. Ten feet from the ocean the engine sputtered to life.

Both men now knew that it would be impossible to reach the Irish coast, even though they had come half the distance. Hawker figured the water in the radiator would be gone in about two hours. He decided to spend this time flying low over the water in search of a ship. Their course had taken them over the shipping lanes. With luck, they might sight a vessel.

The plane's engine was sputtering and bucking. Hawker and Grieve were about drained of hope when they sighted a small Danish freighter, the *Mary* out of Copenhagen. There was no one visible on board. Hawker flew low over the vessel and fired signal flares from his Very pistol. Soon the decks were awash with scurrying figures. Satisfied that the crew was watching, Hawker took the plane about a mile ahead of the ship, then turned and glided down toward it. He "ditched" a few hundred feet from the vessel. The plane was kept afloat by its half empty gas tanks, giving Hawker and Grieve ample time to release their tiny boat and climb into it. The crew of the *Mary* launched a bigger boat to pickup the fliers and bring them aboard.

The flight was over. The *Mary*, however, had no wireless and the world was kept in suspense for a week about the fate of Hawker and Grieve. Great Britain gave the pair a tumultous welcome, surely rivaling in enthusiasm what would have been had their flight been successful. The *Daily Mail* awarded the pair a consolation prize of 5,000 pounds. Several days after their rescue, the American freighter *Lake Charlotteville* came upon a strange bit of flotsam in mid-Atlantic. It was Hawker's plane. The crew hauled the wreckage aboard and carried it back to England. The *Atlantic* made the final stage of the journey in the same manner as her crew—aboard ship.

Read and his NC-4 were at Ponta Delgada when he was told of Hawker's rescue. He and his crew now realized that the competition, in the strict sense of the word, had ended. They merely had to finish to win. They remained at Ponta Delgada for a week making repairs and waiting for the weather to clear. Finally, on May 27, the NC-4 taxied over the bay, lifted into the air, and headed eastward for Lisbon. The weather was perfect. The 781-mile flight was uneventful.

Early in the evening, the voice of co-pilot Elmer Stone came over the intercom. "Commander," he said, "there she is!" Read scanned the horizon. The rocky coast of Portugal was dead ahead. The sight of Europe did not fill Read with great elation, but with relief that a job had been done. He wrote in his log that at 7:31, Greenwich time, on the evening of May 27, 1919, the NC-4, an aircraft of the U.S. Navy, had arrived over Portugal, thus completing, so far as he knew, the first flight over the Atlantic Ocean. Soon afterwards, the plane landed in Lisbon. The flying time from Newfoundland had been twenty-five hours and one minute; the elapsed time had been eleven days.

Although Read took the achievement somewhat in stride, the world at large did not. "We are heartily proud of you," President Wilson wired Read and his crew from Paris, where he was attending a conference.

"You have won the distinction of adding further laurels to our country." Louis Blériot, the French pilot who had been the first to cross the English Channel by air, told newsmen, "Ten years ago my flight was called extraordinary, but it was insignificant compared to the deed of the NC-4."

After a day's stopover, the NC-4 set out for Plymouth. Engine trouble forced the plane down off northern Spain. The crew made repairs and then the flight was resumed. On May 31, they landed in Plymouth.

In Horta, Ponta Delgada, Lisbon and Plymouth, the crew of the NC-4 was honored by receptions and parades. The celebrations continued when they returned to the United States. There were tributes and medals galore. The King of England awarded Read the Royal Air Force Cross, and President Wilson presented him with the Distinguished Flying Medal.

The flight and the men who made it were the nation's No. 1 news story for more than a month, but then settled into relative obscurity. As for the NC-4 itself, Paul Garber, curator of the Air Museum of the Smithsonian Institution, called it "the most overlooked aircraft in history." It was shipped back to the United States not long after the flight to be used in a Navy recruiting tour. Afterwards, it was dismantled and its parts warehoused. Not until after World War II was it resurrected and reassembled. Today it holds a place of honor at the Smithsonian.

CHAPTER
6
ACROSS
NON-STOP

The Atlantic had been crossed by the air for the first time by the U. S. Navy's NC-4. But it had not been crossed non-stop, and Lord Northcliffe's prize was still to be won.

While Hawker and Raynham fidgeted in Newfoundland waiting for a break in the weather, a third team was on its way by ship from England. It was made up of Captain John William Alcock of the Royal Naval Air Service, the pilot, and Lieutenant Arthur William (Ted) Brown of the Royal Air Force, the navigator. The plane they were to fly was a Vickers *Vimy*, a big, powerful converted bomber.

Alcock, at twenty-seven, was one of the most experienced airmen of the day. He had learned to fly while still in his teens, and when World War I erupted, he had already logged more than one-thousand hours. During the war he was put to work instructing RAF pilot candidates. The assignment bored him and he finally managed to get combat duty. He won the Distinguished Flying Cross for his daring low-level bombing of the German cruiser *Goeben*. On another mission his plane's engines failed and he had to ditch in the Aegean Sea. He was captured and thrown into a Turkish prison. After the war he joined Vickers Ltd. as their chief test pilot.

He became enthusiastic about the huge *Vimy*, a bomber that Vickers had put into production just be-

fore the war's end. A biplane, its wings spanned 67 feet, and the fuselage had room enough for four crew members, 3,650 pounds of fuel, and a dozen 250-pound bombs as well. Its twin 360 h.p. Rolls Royce engines could keep the ship aloft for eleven hours. Alcock had often dreamed of flying the Atlantic non-stop. He was certain that this was the ship that could do it.

Alcock went to Vickers officials and proposed an attempt be made at an Atlantic crossing. "It's too late," he was told. "Hawker has his *Atlantic* ready to go. Fred Raynham is also testing a plane. We couldn't be first. Why should we bother to try?"

Alcock had his answer ready. "But the *Vimy* can make the flight almost as she is," he declared. "There's very little that has to be done to her." Then he explained how he would modify the plane. The gun mountings and the bomb racks would be stripped away. Instead of two cockpits in tandem, Alcock would seal over the first and make wider the one behind; there he and his navigator would sit side-by-side. New radio equipment would be installed that would allow the two men to receive messages as well as send them. Finally, additional fuel tanks would be built into the bomb bay. These would increase the *Vimy's* fuel capacity to 868-gallons, giving a maximum range of 2,400 miles. "These changes are simple to make," Alcock told the company's management. "The plane could be ready in two weeks." The directors realized that should one of their planes be the first to make the transatlantic crossing it would be a great boost for the company. They gave Alcock the green light.

Now that he had his plane, Alcock needed a navigator. Experienced navigators were extremely rare, and for a time Alcock considered flying solo and doing the navigating himself. One day Alcock entered the office of Maxwell Muller, the plant manager at Vickers. Muller was interviewing a man for a job as an engineer. The man's name was Ted Brown. Alcock interrupted the interview to make some comment about the fuel tank installation in his plane. Suddenly the man sat up straight. "Were you discussing a flight across the Atlantic?" he asked excitedly. Alcock said that he was.

With that, the man poured out a story of his experiences in the Royal Air Force during the war as an aerial gunner and observer. He told how his two-seater was shot down by German fighters and how the pilot had managed to land the plane without injury to either of them. The Germans then captured the pair. Brown, who had taken a bullet in the foot, was interned in Switzerland. To relieve the boredom during his months of confinement, he studied navigation. He was aware of the Lord Northcliffe prize, and had compiled a mass of calculations and charts concerning the cross-ocean flight. One day he hoped to make the crossing. However, his wartime injury had left him with a limp. For this reason, Sopwith and Martinsyde, other companies planning a transatlantic flight, had rejected him. But to Alcock, Brown's lameness meant nothing. "Throw away your cane," he told him. "The way we're going, you won't need it."

Alcock and Brown sailed on the *Mauretania* for St. John's, Newfoundland, early in May to make preliminary arrangements. The plane was to arrive on a merchant ship two weeks later. Like Hawker and Raynham, they were wholly unprepared for Newfoundland's gray wintry skies and general gloominess. They were also startled to learn that the countryside offered nothing in the way of land that could be prepared for an airstrip. Alcock and Brown rented a car and began a search. Many of the natives felt that the British airmen had unlimited funds, and one offered Alcock the use of a pasture at the rate of $200 a day!

On the Sunday after Alcock and Brown arrived, Hawker made his attempt. On Monday they waited for the announcement that he had arrived in Ireland. But no news came that day, nor the next. It was late in the week before they learned that Hawker had been rescued after his crash-landing at sea.

Raynham, who had ruined his machine in his attempt to take off, gen-

erously gave over his field to Alcock. It had to be considerably length-
ened for the big *Vimy*, and Alcock hired a crew of workers with picks
and shovels to remove the boulders and trees and fill the ditches. When
the plane arrived, the field was ready. Early in June, Alcock put the plane
through two successful test flights. Days of gale winds and heavy rains
followed the second trial. Alcock announced that as soon as the weather
cleared, he would go.

He was taking no chances. He recalled what caused Hawker to be
forced down, so he ordered that every drop of gasoline put into the
Vimy's tanks be filtered through a fine mesh screen. Both radiators were
drained and flushed. Alcock packed a Very pistol for signaling and a
flashlight in the small compartment behind his seat. He also regarded as
vital to the crossing two toy black cats, Lucky Jim and Twinkletoes.
Lucky Jim wore an expression of cheerful confidence. Twinkletoes, however, expressed anxiety.

On the afternoon of June 13, 1919, Alcock was brought the news that
the following day would bring clear skies and westerly winds, and the
favorable weather would extend all the way from Newfoundland to
the Irish coast. Alcock grinned. "That's what we've been waiting to
hear," he said. "We'll be off tomorrow." But when he awoke just after
dawn, a forty mile-an-hour gale was blowing. It was the very same quart-
ering wind that had worked to demolish Raynham's Martinsyde. Alcock
and Brown had no choice but to wait. They squatted on the grass beneath the airplane wing and had their lunch. The news of their impend-
ing take off had spread quickly through St. John's and virtually the entire population had descended upon the field. They spread their picnic
lunches and the smoke rose from the small fires they built to brew their
tea.

Around noontime the wind died down and shifted to a westerly direction. Alcock gave the word for departure. The two airmen slipped
into their bulky flying suits and pulled on their fur-lined leather helmets.
Then they climbed into the plane, Alcock on the port side, Brown on the
starboard. Members of the crew scurried down the field to warn the onlookers to keep a safe distance.

The port engine was started with no difficulty. Then the starboard.

Alcock pressed the throttle forward, running up the engines to full power. Then he raised his gloved hand and moved it in an arc through the air. Mechanics crouching behind the wings, their backs turned to the propeller wash, jerked hard on ropes that pulled the chocks from the wheels. Instantly the *Vimy* lurched ahead. The crowd on the side-lines cheered.

The takeoff run was up a slight incline with a thick row of hedges at the end. The turf was spongy in spots. The plane gained speed with agonizing slowness. At 500 yards, Alcock felt the tail come up, but the wheels were still on the ground. At 600 yards, he felt the wheels lift off, but then bounce back. The hedge was dead ahead. At the last possible second, the plane lifted sluggishly into the air. The wheels missed the hedge by inches.

Alcock let the *Vimy* dip downward for a moment, gathering speed. When he did so, the plane disappeared behind a grassy knoll. "She's down!" cried spectators, and they started running. But seconds later the plane reappeared and she was climbing steadily. When the altimeter reported 300 feet, Alcock put the craft into a gentle turn and pointed the nose toward the open ocean. Brown sent the flight's first message. "All well, and started," it said.

The westerly wind was a great boon, for it added as much as thirty miles an hour to the plane's cruising speed. This was one of the trip's rare blessings, however. Visibility was an acute problem. As soon as they had cleared land, the plane ran into fog. Alcock climbed above the fog bank only to find that the sun was block out by thick clouds. They remained sandwiched in between the solid layers of fog and clouds for several hours.

Brown's sextant and most of his other navigational instruments were useless. He had to depend solely on dead reckoning, that is, on compass readings and data he recorded in his log—speed, course and the distance traveled—rather than on more accurate astronomical observations. He was also hampered because he could not see the ocean waves to determine which way the wind was blowing, and thus he could not figure out the plane's angle of drift.

Brown decided he would send a message reporting their progress. He reeled out the antenna, unlocked the transmitter and began tapping. He could tell at once that the set was dead. He checked the connections but could find nothing wrong. Then he looked out on the wing. The tiny propeller that drove the wireless generator was gone. Even if Brown had had a spare propeller, it would not have been possible to climb out and install it. The flight was not yet one hour old, and already they were without communications and their most sophisticated navigational aids were of no value.

Suddenly the steady drone of the engines was broken by a loud staccato burst from the starboard side. It sounded like the firing of a machine gun. Brown, closest to the engine, could see that a section of exhaust pipe had broken loose and was swiveling back and forth from the engine nacelle. Then it broke off and dropped away leaving the cylinders to exhaust directly into the open air. It was an anxious moment. Would the engine flames light the wing on fire? Both men held their breath. Nothing happened. The engine roared on, at a higher pitch, to be sure, but the bright plume of flame proved to be no hazard.

Just before darkness fell, the *Vimy* shot out of the clouds and into bright sun. Quickly Brown took a reading. His calculations showed that only a slight course correction was necessary. The clouds then enveloped them again. Around midnight Brown was able to take his sights on the North Star and Vega. He found that they had flown more than a thousand miles. They were now well beyond "the point of no return."

Time dragged. The batteries that powered their electrically heating flying suits had long since failed. The frigid air chilled them to the bones. But their greatest physical discomfort came from their cramped legs and arms. Alcock had to sit like a robot, without taking his hands from the control column or his feet from the rudder bar. Brown, with his bad leg, found every movement to be agony. The flight was surely an endurance contest.

With the first gray glow of dawn, the monotony was shattered. The tall black clouds of a ferocious storm loomed just ahead. It began to rain. Angry gusts shook the plane, and Alcock strained with every ounce of strength he had remaining to keep the ship under control. The sky was lighted by jagged streaks of lightning. Hail beat a tattoo on the wings and stabbed at the fliers' cheeks.

Alcock, without a point of reference outside, no longer knew the ship's attitude. Suddenly the plane stalled, paused motionless for an instant, and then nosed over into a deadly dive. Alcock kept his eyes glued to the altimeter. It read 4,000 feet, then 3,000, then 2,000—and they continued to spiral seaward. At 500 feet, they broke from the clouds. Alcock pulled back on the control column. The engines fired. He opened both throttles wide. As they leveled off, they could feel salty spray upon their faces.

Alcock climbed to 9,000 feet. The controls felt sluggish, and the engine sound grew labored. Brown put down his logbook and grabbed his flashlight. He pointed the thin beam onto the wing. It confirmed what they both knew—ice!

Ice had frozen the ailerons. Worse, it was beginning to clog the engine air intake ducts. An engine needs air just as a human being needs food. Already power and speed were beginning to dwindle.

Brown knew what had to be done if the plane were to stay aloft. The ice had to be cleared away. And, crippled or not, he peeled off his gloves. Suddenly Alcock realized what Brown was planning. He tried to pull him back but Brown tugged away.

He stepped from the cockpit to the open wing and felt a stinging burst of freezing air. He clung to the wing wires and struts as he inched his way toward the engine. With one arm crooked about a strut, he reached up to hack at the ice with a jackknife. The huge four-bladed propeller whirred only inches from his hand. He grew numb with cold but he would not quit. At last the intake duct was clear. Alcock felt the sudden surge of power.

Brown then made his way back to the cockpit. But his nightmare was not over. The intake duct on the other side had to be freed. Out on the treacherous port wing he went. He grabbed a strut for support and chopped. Somehow the job was done.

At dawn the *Vimy* was still enshrouded in great banks of clouds too high to climb over. Conditions remained tensed for the next three or four hours. Sleet choked the radiator shutters and caused the tachometer and fuel gauge to fail.

At 11,000 feet the sun shone for a few moments, and Brown was able to get a navigational fix. It revealed that they were slightly north of their intended course, but close to the Irish coast. Alcock took the plane down hoping to find a break in the clouds, and at the same time turned south, toward Galway, their original destination. Brown reached for something to drink. He replaced the lid on the empty thermos jug and had turned to replace it in the small compartment behind his seat. Suddenly Alcock grabbed him by the shoulder and twisted him forward. He was pointing ahead and below. His lips were moving frantically but the roar of the engines wiped away his words. Then Brown saw two tiny specks of green—land! He grabbed his charts. The tiny specks were the islands Eashal and Turbut, and just beyond were the peaks of Connemara, north of Galway Bay. Brown had brought the flight to within twenty-five miles of its intended landfall, an incredible bit of navigation.

Alcock urged the *Vimy* up over the cliff-lined coast and headed toward the towering mast of the Clifden wireless station. As he circled the station, Brown fired two flares from their Very pistol. A man appeared waving his arms wildly. Near the station, Alcock spotted a level green field. He put the plane into a smooth glide. It was a perfect approach. He cut the engines and eased back on the control column. The wheels touched down.

But the plane jerked to a sudden stop, tipped forward, and buried its nose in soft ground. The green level field was not a field at all but a treacherous Irish peat bog. Fortunately, neither Alcock or Brown was injured. Their flight had come to an end at 8:40 A.M. on Sunday, June 15. The pair had flown slightly over 1,900 miles in sixteen hours and fifty-seven minutes, an average speed of 118 m.p.h.

In his account of the flight, Brown said that his greatest disappointment was that nobody had tried to reach them by radio during the trip. While he was unable to transmit messages, his wireless was capable of receiving them, but all he ever heard was ships talking to one another about commonplace matters. It seemed to him that the whole world was oblivious to their flight.

But once the plane touched down, it was a different story. Hundreds of thousands of Londoners lined city streets to cheer the pair two days after their arrival. Each was knighted by King George V, and the *Vimy* was enshrined at the Science Museum in South Kensington. The fliers were given the 10,000 pounds *Daily Mail* prize by the secretary of War,

Winston Churchill, who compared what they had done with Columbus' discovery of America.

Said Churchill: "It is an event which shows that while we have become more powerfully equipped with engineering and scientific apparatus, we have also preserved as a race the audacity, the courage, the physical qualities of the old heroic bygone times.

"I really do not know what we should admire most in our guests," Churchill continued, becoming a bit mischievous, "their audacity, their skill, their science, the Vickers *Vimy* airplane, their Rolls engines—or their good fortune."

CHAPTER 7 LINDY

Charles Augustus Lindbergh was, of course, the first man to fly alone across the Atlantic Ocean. His flight took him from Roosevelt Field on Long Island, not far from New York City, to Le Bourget, an airport just northeast of Paris. He arrived late in the evening of May 21, 1927. The distance he covered was approximately 3,600 miles. The time of the trip was 33 hours, 30 minutes.

It must be said at once that this was not really a landmark achievement in the history of aviation. Bold, yes; brave, yes; important, yes. But not monumental. After all, the Atlantic had been crossed several times before. U.S. Navy aviators had made the flight as early as 1919. It was not the first nonstop flight. Alcock and Brown had won that honor.

Yet when the wheels of Lindbergh's plane, *The Spirit of St. Louis*, touched down upon the soft earth of Le Bourget, it set off a global celebration that has never been equalled in intensity.

Nineteen countries conferred awards upon the young man. The United States decorated him with three medals, including the Medal of Honor, the nation's highest award, and the Distinguished Flying Cross. President Coolidge dispatched the cruiser *Memphis* to Europe to bring Lindy back to the United States. When the vessel steamed up Chesapeake Bay, she was accompanied by four destroyers, a pair of Army blimps and forty airplanes. Then came the award ceremony in

Washington. It attracted the greatest crowd ever assembled in the city's history.

The next day there was a tickertape parade in New York City, ceremonies at City Hall and later in Central Park. The city was swept with a kind of hysteria. Four million people turned out to cheer the smiling, boyish hero. His likeness stared down from countless posters, and signs proclaiming "Welcome Home, Lindy" were plastered everywhere. Hawkers and sidewalk salesmen had a field day. His image was painted on canvas, etched in copper, cast in molten lead ("while you wait"), crocheted in yarn, scissored in black paper and interpreted in frosting and French pastry.

Several times during that frantic day crowds broke through police barriers in their efforts to touch him. When the figure of Lindbergh appeared on the screen in a newsreel at the Roxy Theatre, the six thousand customers stood and cheered. The usually staid New York *Times* printed Lindbergh's name in headlines of the size usually reserved for wars or armstices. Some psychologists have come to call all of this adulation the "Lindbergh phenomenon."

Looking back, it is not hard to uncover the reasons for this remarkable outpouring of emotion. Foremost was Lindbergh himself. In appearance and personality, he was the epitome of the American hero of the day—handsome, young (he was 25), tall (a shade over six-feet), clean-cut, curly-haired and straight-jawed. He smiled easily, and he had great charm and grace. (When the Aero Club of France awarded him 150,000 francs in honor of his flight, he promptly donated the prize to the families of French pilots who "had died for aviation.")

Lindbergh's background was tinged with glamor and excitement. He was born in Detroit on February 4, 1902, and was brought up in Little Falls, Minnesota. Aviation became his great love, and he dropped out of the University of Wisconsin during his sophomore year to enroll as a flying student with the Nebraska Aircraft Corporation. Next he barnstormed as a "wing-walker" and performed as a parachute jumper. The first plane he owned was a war surplus Jenny. He paid $500 for it. He junketed through Mississippi and parts of Texas, stopping at small towns, and offering the crowds of curious that gathered passenger flights at five dollars a piece. He made a good living. In 1924, he enlisted as a cadet in the U.S. Army Air Corps and was commissioned a second lieutenant. Later he joined the Air Mail Service and became chief pilot on the Chicago-St. Louis route. Newspaper accounts of his career never overlooked the fact that he had made four emergency parachute jumps. While flying the mail one night in the fall of 1926, the idea of an Atlantic crossing by air struck him. Soon after, he secured financial backing for the venture from a group of St. Louis businessmen.

There was a second overriding factor in the great eminence that Lindbergh achieved. During the early months of 1927, four other planes were preparing to fly the Atlantic. In other words, it was a race, but the most spectacular race of all time—3,600 miles across open ocean. "When will they go? Who will be the first to leave?" were questions on everyone's lips.

Much of the incentive behind these flights was a $25,000 prize that had been put up by Raymond Orteig for the first flight from New York to Paris. Orteig had made the offer in 1919, not long after the Alcock-Brown crossing. To Lindbergh, however, the money was secondary. The flight itself was what counted.

Among the other "contestants" was Navy Commander Noel Davis, who had received $100,000 in financial backing from the American Legion, and was planning to make the flight in a redesigned Army bomber. Davis seemed likely to start first, but he and his co-pilot crashed during a trial flight and both were killed. Early in May that year, an attempt was launched by French war ace Charles Nungesser and his co-pilot François Coli. They took off from Paris, were reported over England, and never heard from again. Ships and aircraft scoured the water of the

North Atlantic for the pair, and day by day concern mounted. United States ambassador to France, Myron Herrick, asked American pilots who were considering transatlantic flights to shelve their plans "out of regard for the present state of anxiety (of the French)." The ambassador's request fell on deaf ears.

Now, besides Lindbergh, two competitors remained. One was a man named Charles Levine. He had purchased a Bellanca equipped with a Wright Whirlwind engine, and, since he was not a pilot himself, had obtained the services of Clarence Chamberlin, an experienced airman. Navigator Lloyd Bertraud was another member of the Levine team.

Commander Richard Byrd was another of Lindbergh's challengers. Byrd had the backing of Rodman Wanamaker, the wealthy department store owner.

In comparison to Chamberlin and Byrd and their backers, Lindbergh was something of a poverty case. His plane was smaller and less powerful. He was the underdog. Of course, Americans have always adored underdogs.

Lindbergh knew exactly the type of plane he wanted. He preferred the monoplane style, even though it was just coming into vogue, because he knew that it could fly faster and carry a greater load per square foot of wing surface than a biplane. But getting a plane was a problem. He had his heart set on the Bellanca with the Wright engine, but the Wright Company refused to sell him the plane. He next went to Giuseppe Bellanca, the man who had built the plane and sold it to the Wright Company. "Could you build me another just like the first?" Lindbergh asked. Bellanca refused "I'll build you a plane," he said, "but it'll have to be a three-engine ship, and it'll cost you $29,000."

This was almost twice as much as Lindbergh was prepared to pay, but even if he had had the money, it's doubtful that he would have made the purchase. Lindy had little regard for three-engined ships, although many people of the day considered them a great deal safer. Lindy's backers felt this way, and had suggested that he consider purchasing a three-engined ship of the type that Anton Fokker had built for Commander Byrd.

Lindbergh knew, of course, that in case one engine failed that a tri-motored plane could continue to stay aloft on two engines, although some of the fuel supply had to be jettisoned. Lindbergh looked at the other side of the coin. "A three-motored plane," he argued, "had three times the chance of motor failure." He also pointed out that a plane with three engines has much greater head resistance to the air and therefore less cruising range. Lindbergh's arguments convinced everyone; a single engine monoplane it would be.

But whose? After the Wright Company turned him down, and then Bellanca, Lindbergh next went to see a representative of the Fokker Company. He was told that building a single-engined plane was out of the question. Lindbergh did not even bother to try the Boeing or Douglas Companies. He knew that they would be unwilling to sell a single-engined plane to someone with his lack of reputation, a young man who was surely going to kill himself, to the great detriment of the company's name. It was almost out of desperation that Lindy contacted the Ryan Company, a small aircraft manufacturer in San Diego, California.

Ryan had less than a dozen employees and operated out of a rundown waterfront warehouse. The company had no flying field and so had to truck its planes through city streets to an open area on the edge of town to test fly them. Lindbergh went out to San Diego to place the order, and then remained in California for the two months that it took to build the ship. He was at once impressed by the Ryan personnel. They threw themselves wholeheartedly into the project and worked day and night, seven days a week.

At first, Donald Hall, Ryan's chief engineer, disagreed with Lindbergh that he should make the trip alone. Hall did not believe that any pilot could stay awake for the estimated forty hours it would take to get to Paris. But Lindbergh declared that he had often stayed awake forty hours and even more when carrying the mail. He insisted he did not want a passenger. "A co-pilot or navigator, his equipment, and a cockpit for him to sit in means another 250 or 300 pounds," said Lindbergh. "I'd rather see that weight given over to additional gasoline." At length, Hall agreed.

Lindbergh purchased a Wright Whirlwind engine for the ship that cost about $4,000. The plane itself cost $6,000. The total outlay was thus well within Lindbergh's budget. The plane had a 46-foot wingspan, and in its five gas tanks it could carry 450 gallons of gasoline. Its largest fuel tank was built into the fuselage to get it positioned properly, the pilot's compartment had to be moved back, behind the nose tank. The tank was too big to see over, and rather than lean to the side in the cockpit, Lindy had a periscope installed to allow him to see ahead.

Nothing was taken that was not vitally necessary to the operation of the plane. There was no radio. Lindbergh judged the resultant saving in weight to be of greater value than communications. He did not want fuel-tank gauges. He thought them to be a safety hazard. He would keep track of his fuel supply with a watch and a record of engine revolutions. A parachute? Why brother? The route he was taking offered hardly any place to land, and the chute weighed ten extra pounds. In case of an emergency, he planned to inflate a rubber life raft, one that he could inflate with a hand pump in a few minutes. It weighed ten pounds. He would take to the raft if the plane sank. He got four red flares and sealed each in a watertight piece of rubber tubing. He bought a match safe and matches and two flashlights.

His food supply consisted of five tins of concentrated Army emergency rations, plus a gallon container of water.

During the period when the plane was being built, Lindbergh spent most of his time working out the navigational details of the trip. He knew the shortest route to Europe to be a great circle route that would take him northeast out of New York, across Cape Cod, Nova Scotia and Newfoundland, and then on to Paris. He bought a hydrographic chart of the North Atlantic and plotted his course upon it, with bearings at intervals of one-hundred miles, the distance he figured he would fly in one hour. Of course, he compensated for magnetic variations that would affect his compass and prevailing winds. Lindbergh fully realized that his methods lacked the accuracy of celestial navigation, but he felt the additional fuel he could carry much more valuable than a navigator.

He figured out that he could arrive over the coast of Europe a full three-hundred miles off course—anywhere in between southern Scandinavia and northern Spain—and still have fuel enough remaining to reach Paris. He took special pains to commit to memory the coastline characteristics of the various countries of Western Europe. Ireland's terrain was somewhat mountainous; England was rather hilly on the southern end; France was low along the coast, and Spain was mountainous. Once he had established which country he was flying over, he would obtain an accurate position from the contours of the coastline and by the placement of the towns, rivers and railroads.

On April 28, sixty days after the order had been placed, the *Spirit of St. Louis* was ready for its test flight. She performed splendidly. In the days that followed, Lindbergh made load and weight tests with the ship, and prepared for his nonstop flight to St. Louis, where his backers had planned a welcoming celebration. Then it was on to New York. He arrived at Curtiss Field on Long Island late in the afternoon of May 13, 1927.

The time that Lindbergh spent in New York City before his departure gave an indication of what was to come. Whenever he appeared on the city streets, clusters of people followed him. (He was easy to recognize; he wore riding breeches, a wool shirt and golf socks.) Thousands of New Yorkers made the trek out to Curtiss Field in hopes of seeing Lindy and his plane. Whenever he was spotted, the throng would burst into spontaneous applause. One night some of Lindy's admirers climbed to the roof of a maintenance building adjacent to the hangar that housed his plane to get a better view inside. The perch became so popular that the building collapsed.

Poor weather caused many days of delay. On May 19, the weather was still bad, and reports from ships along the great circle route were unfavorable. Lindbergh spent the morning visiting the Wright Company's plant in Paterson, New Jersey, and in the evening planned to attend the theatre with some friends. But around six o'clock he received a special report from the weather bureau. The North Atlantic was clearing, it said. Lindbergh forgot the theatre and hurried at once to Curtiss Field.

He gave instructions to service and check the plane, and around midnight went to his hotel to rest. Sleep would not come. At three A.M. he returned to the hangar.

Mist hung low over the field and a light rain was falling. The plane had to be taken to adjacent Roosevelt Field, which offered a better runway. His mechanics wrapped the engine in a tarpaulin and lifted the plane's tailskid onto the back of a truck then towed the ship tail first. A tank truck with fuel, police on motorcycles, some newspapermen, and a few bystanders formed the ghostly procession that made its way through the rain and darkness. Lindbergh said it reminded him of a funeral.

By seven A.M., the shower had passed, although the sky was still gray. At 7:40 A.M., the plane's motor was started. Twelve minutes later Charles Lindbergh left for Paris.

It is a tribute to Lindbergh's careful planning that so much of the trip was uneventful. Before he reached Cape Cod, the weather had cleared and visibility was excellent. He sighted the coast of Nova Scotia by noon. Comparing the terrain with his map, he found that he was only six miles off course. His speed was averaging slightly more than one-hundred miles an hour, and his use of fuel was about what he had anticipated. He passed over St. John's, Newfoundland, and then headed out over the Atlantic.

Darkness came, and then a low fog obscured the water. It became thicker, and Lindbergh took the plane to ten-thousand feet to escape the cover. There was no moon at first, although he could see the stars. Once during the night, ice began to collect on the wings. He quickly detoured from his course to seek warmer air.

Later on, Lindy's earth inductor compass acted queerly. This instrument is set for the desired course. When the plane is flying on that course, the indicator on the compass dial holds at zero. Something went wrong. Lindbergh watched in horror as the needle swept back and forth—not even pausing at zero. He didn't know if he was half asleep and imagining what was happening or whether the instrument was really failing.

Then he turned to the magnetic compass hanging over his head. This, too, was swinging wildly. But he observed that the magnetic compass hesitated between oscillations, that it sometimes remained steady for several seconds at a time. So he set his heading by the periods of hesitations. "God only knows," he thought, "where I'll strike the European coast."

Lindbergh's greatest problem was the threat of sleep. He had not slept for almost twenty-four hours before his takeoff. Through the long night and into the day that followed, he waged an almost constant struggle to keep his mind alert and his body awake. "If my plane can stay aloft, if my engines can keep running, so can I," he thought to himself. Mere determination was not enough, however. He felt he never wanted anything so much in his life as he wanted to close his eyes, and to fight off the desire he cupped his hand and held it in the slipstream to divert the chill air into his face. He tilted his head back and breathed deeply until his lungs were full. He drew the collar of his flying suit tight to his throat against the cold. Yet he would not replace the cockpit windows, feeling that once he shut out the outside air, the clouds and the sky, sleep would surely overpower him.

There is a cushion of air close to the earth through which a plane can fly with less effort than at high altitude. The next day Lindbergh spent hours at a time flying through this layer. Sometimes he was within ten feet of the waves. He watched the white caps closely. When one crested and the wind whipped the spray, it gave him an indication of the wind's direction and velocity, and from these he got a general idea of the plane's drift.

Lindy expected that daylight would ease his almost overpowering desire for sleep, but he was wrong. The torture continued through the long morning and into the afternoon. There were times that he slept with his eyes open, his hands like those of a robot on the controls. He would be startled into wakefulness by an abrupt change in the plane's altitude or direction.

It was not until the flight was in in its twenty-seventh hour that the craving for sleep left him. He saw a black speck on the horizon. Gradually it took form. A fishing boat! The European coast could not be far off.

Then he saw that the boat was but one of a small fleet. He circled low over it but saw no signs of life. He tried a second time and spotted a man's face at the cabin window. More than once Lindy had carried on a conversation with people on the ground by flying low, throttling down the engine, shouting out a question and receiving the answer by signal. Now he tried it. He glided to within a few feet of the boat, and leaned his head out of the window. "Which way to Ireland?" he screamed. The man stared dumbly. "Probably doesn't understand English," Lindy thought. He gunned the engine and resumed his course.

A few minutes later a fringe of coastline appeared. It was barren and somewhat mountainous. He felt sure it was Ireland. He climbed to two-thousand feet to get a more commanding view. He scanned the shore, then the chart in his lap. Suddenly his face burst into a wide smile. The outline of the coast corresponded to Cape Valencia south of Dingle Bay —southwestern Ireland. He had traveled more than three thousand miles and was but three miles off course.

Paris was still six hours away. But it would be simple. He passed over southern Ireland, over St. George's Channel to England's southeastern tip just south of Plymouth. He crossed the English Channel to strike France at Cherbourg. Visibility was good, and there were landmarks now —towns, roads and railways. Lindy could navigate the way he knew best. All of France had been alerted to his arrival. As he passed over villages, the people flooded into the streets. Most only heard the roar of his engine, for the sun had faded. Lindbergh was beginning his second night aloft.

Beneath him now was the River Seine, glistening in the darkness. He followed it. In the distance there was a soft glow, the lights of Paris. A few minutes later he circled the Eiffel Tower. The airport—Le Bourget —did not appear on his map. He saw an open area that he thought to be an airport, but he was not sure. It seemed too close to Paris to be Le Bourget. To make sure there was no other field, he flew four or five miles northeast. When he saw no other field, he returned. Several times he circled low, very low. He spotted a hangar, then some others, and even a wind sock. And something else—long lines of automobile headlights, an endless traffic jam that stretched from the field all the way back to Paris. Lindbergh's welcoming committee was gathering.

Lindbergh circled the field once, then headed into the wind to land. He had never before landed the *Spirit of St. Louis* at night, but he had no difficulty. Over the hangar roofs he came. The wheels touched gently. The tail skid made contact. Lindbergh jolted along in the darkness, not quite sure of what was ahead. As the *Spirit of St. Louis* stopped rolling, Lindbergh turned the plane around and started to head back toward the floodlit hangars.

Suddenly he stopped and cut the engine. He rubbed his eyes in disbelief. Fifty-thousand Frenchmen had routed ranks of soldiers, broken through the police lines, trampled down a stout iron fence and now they were rushing toward the plane. A great wave of cheers went up when they saw him. They dragged Lindy from the cockpit and carried him on their shoulders. The "Lindbergh phenomenon" had begun.

CHAPTER
8
CHAL-LENGING THE PACIFIC

Once the Atlantic had been crossed, and then spanned non-stop, the next obvious test was the Pacific. An Australian, Charles E. Kingsford-Smith, was one of the first pilots to give serious thought to a transpacific crossing.

In 1920, Smith went to the United States to raise money for such a venture. Although only twenty-one, Smith had an impressive record as a flier, including experience in the RAF during World War I. He was a rangy, well-muscled young man, and his face and manner bespoke confidence and determination. People listened to his pleas for financial support. But all he got for his efforts were indulgent smiles, never any money.

"Smithy," as his friends called him, returned to Australia and his job as a pilot with Sydney's Interstate Flying Services, but he never relinquished his dream. Then chance threw Smith into a meeting with Charles T. P. Ulm, a rugged-looking, dark-haired airman, whose ambitions to cross the Pacific matched his own. Smith and Ulm began to plan the flight together.

By 1927, long distance flights over oceans were no longer thought to be quite so fanciful. Lindbergh's stirring dash across the Atlantic had done much to change the public's attitude. After Lindbergh, Europe was deluged with visitors from America's skies. In June 1927, Clarence Chamberlin and Charles Levine piloted a Bellanca single-motored monoplane non-stop from New

York to Eiselben, a city only 118 miles from Berlin. Commander Richard Byrd and his crew of three made the crossing in their Fokker a few weeks later (although the Byrd craft was forced down 200 feet from the French coast).

Smith and Ulm also made aviation headlines in 1927 by becoming the first to fly around the Australian continent. On the day they landed in Sydney completing their trip, a luncheon was given in their honor. Speaker after speaker lauded the pair. When it became Kingsford-Smith's turn at the rostrum, he told the gathering of his long-cherished ambition to fly the Pacific. And he did more. He made a public appeal for funds to enable him and Ulm to make the crossing. Within a week, the Australian government came forward with a pledge of 3,500 pounds, and there were many other promises of support. Now it was up to Kingsford-Smith and Ulm. Could they turn their dreams into reality?

In mid-July they sailed on the steamer *Tahiti*, arriving in San Francisco early in August. They found the entire West Coast bubbling with excitement over the Dole Derby. Contestants were to fly from the West Coast of the United States to Hawaii. James D. Dole, the sponsor of the race, was offering a purse of $25,000 to the winner and $10,000 to the pilot who finished second. Critics said that the prizes were too tempting, that they were certain to attract fliers who had only limited mechanical skills or a lack of over-the-water navigational experience. Or both. The critics were right. The race is a dismal and tragic footnote in the history of American aviation. Fifteen planes entered; eight managed to get into the air and only two arrived at the goal.

Three machines crashed in preliminary flights, killing three men. Two other planes crashed on taking off, and two just simply disappeared.

That's not all; two men lost their lives searching for downed planes. In total, the Dole fiasco took ten lives, and achieved little if anything in the scientific advance of aviation.

A period of great gloom descended upon the aviation industry. Many people now believed that flying was synonymous with death, and this attitude placed a heavy burden on the two Australians as they sought to line-up additional money and backing for their flight.

The outcome of the Dole Race did nothing to dim the enthusiasm of Smith and Ulm. They were just as certain as ever that the transpacific flight could be made, providing they could obtain the right plane and properly equip it. The Dole contest had confirmed what the two Australians had suspected—a single engine plane was not the craft for a transpacific flight.

A study of successful ocean flights showed clearly that the Wright Whirlwind engine and Fokker aircraft had attained a high level of achievement. Byrd's plane was a three-motored Fokker. Lindbergh's plane had been equipped with a Wright Whirlwind; so had the craft used by Chamberlin and Levine. Probably the most convincing evidence was the first nonstop flight over the Pacific from the mainland of the United States to Hawaii. It was made in June 1927, by a pair of Army lieutenants, Lester J. Maitland and Albert F. Hegenberger, and they had used a plane very similar to Byrd's, a three-motored Fokker.

A large plane, such as a Fokker, would enable Smith and Ulm to increase their crew to four, including a radioman and a navigator. They were now convinced that skillful navigation was as vital to the success of their flight as fuel and a take off strip. But a big Fokker meant more money, much more than they had originally planned on. They launched a new appeal for funds.

One of the first men that they approached was Sidney Myer, a well known Australian businessman. At first, Myer would have no part of their venture. He felt sure it was going to cost both pilots their lives. But he finally relented, and handed the pair $1,500. "It's not a loan," Myer said, "It's a gift."

A few days later the two men received a telephone call from Myer. "Look," he said, "You have the money: it's yours. Put it in your pockets;

keep it. But please do not risk your lives in that foolish flight. Please forget about it."

Such was the temper of the times. Myer's pleas, however, had little effect upon either Smith or Ulm.

Sir George Hubert Wilkins, Australian explorer of the Arctic and Antarctic, was the next man to offer a helping hand. He called the pair from Seattle to tell them that he had a Fokker, but without instruments and engines. Would they be interested in buying it at half the original purchase price? The two pilots snapped up the offer.

The Fokker was an impressive looking plane. It weighed almost six tons and could haul ten passengers. The fuselage was constructed of welded aluminum and was fifty feet in length. The plane's main feature was its thick, 72-foot wing that was sheeted with plywood. Smith and Ulm named the ship the *Southern Cross* after the constellation that symbolizes the South Pacific.

The next step was to get three Whirlwind engines. They soon learned the Wright factory was backlogged with almost one hundred engine orders, which meant an extremely long wait. But Smith had a plan. He and Ulm would borrow three engines from the United States military authorities, and when the three that they had ordered from Wright came off the assembly line they would be turned over to the military to repay the "loan."

It was not easy getting the military to agree to the plan, and the two pilots were subjected to some rude treatment. "You're crazy," an American admiral told the pair. "The Navy is spending hundreds of thousands of dollars hunting for those fliers lost in the Dole race. We don't want any more pilots lost. Cancel your plans;" he urged, "forget them."

But when Smith and Ulm disclosed that they planned to use a three-engined Fokker, the American military had a change of heart. " 'Three-motored Fokker,' those were magic words," Smith observed. The engines were delivered.

As one problem was solved, another sprang up to take its place. Shortly after news of the Dole Race reached Australia, Smith and Ulm received cable messages from Australia's newspapers asking the pair to abandon their flight. Then came a request from the Australian government directing the two men to cancel their plans and take the first steamer home. But Smith and Ulm knew they could not turn back now. They pushed on with their plans.

Financial troubles continued to plague the pair, and they became so acute that Smith and Ulm had to agree to sell the Fokker to satisfy the demands of creditors. It began to look as if the trip would never take place. Then the pair received new backing in Los Angeles and were able to repurchase the plane. By the end of May 1928, all was in readiness for their departure.

Smith was to captain the flight; Ulm was to be co-commander and relief pilot. Two Americans were also in the crew. Harry Lyon was to serve as navigator and Jim Warner as radioman. Smith and Ulm were seated side-by-side within the almost totally enclosed cockpit. To rest, each had to stretch out horizontally in his seat. The navigator and radioman had a closet-sized cabin, with a large chart table and the radio equipment. There was room enough on the floor to lie down.

The flight was one of the first to rely heavily on the use of radio. The finest equipment available was installed, enabling the *Southern Cross* to receive beacon signals from both shore stations and ships.

There seemed to be one basic flaw in the planning, however. Critics wanted to know why Smith and Ulm had chosen a land plane for what was essentially an over-the-water flight. One reason was economics; the cost of an amphibious plane was far beyond their budget. Besides, the two Australians were very much impressed by the reliability record of trimotored Fokkers. They knew that if one engine failed at any stage of the flight, they could still reach land. Even if two engines failed, the one remaining engine would keep them in the air for two or three hours.

Should the plane be forced down at sea, the crew planned to rely on the wood-covered 72-foot wing to keep them afloat. They carried saws with which they intended to cut loose the fuselage and the two outboard engines to make the wing more floatable. Emergency rations and a battery-operated radio transmitter were stored in the wing. They felt certain that they would be able to ride it to safety.

The crew planned to make the journey in three hops. The first was to be from Mills Field in Oakland to Wheeler Field in Hawaii. Suva, in the

Fiji Islands, 3,100 miles to the south and west, was to be the next stop. This was the longest hop. From Suva, they planned to fly to Brisbane on Australia's east coast.

Several hundred people were at Mills Field on the morning of May 31, 1928, to watch the *Southern Cross* depart. When Smith took his seat at the controls, a rush of people gathered about him for a final handshake. Then the three engines were cranked up and Smith nosed the plane down the runway. At 8:54 A.M. the wheels left the ground. The ship climbed to a thousand feet, then swept out over the sea where it was quickly swallowed up in the gray curtain of mist that shrouded the Golden Gate.

In the hectic final minutes before the flight's departure, someone had given the crew a tiny silk Australian flag. Smith fixed it on the instrument panel between the gasoline gauges. It fluttered gaily at first but the rushing wind soon began to fray the silk. No man in the crew had the courage to strike the flag, and slowly the shreds of silk began to vanish in the wind. Finally, only the tiny flagstaff remained.

Besides the wind, there was the noise. The thunderous roar of the engines drowned out all attempts to converse. The only way to communicate was by writing out messages. When Lyon and Warner in the navigator's cabin wanted to inquire about the plane's course, they scribbled a note, pinned it to a stick and poked the stick into the pilot's cockpit. It was a bizarre experience for four men to be together in so small a space yet not be able to exchange a word.

The weather bureau had given the flight an optimistic report. The forecast was for light following winds for the first 400 miles of the 2,400 mile journey and moderate headwinds. The skies were to be clear; not a hint of a disturbance was predicted.

In the early hours of the flight, the crew was mentally occupied. "Is everything all right?" was the question that ran through the mind of each man. Each listened intently to the beat of the engines. Each was alert to the plane's every pitch or yaw. Once they became confident that every part of the craft was working as it should, monotony began to build.

The engines thundered endlessly. The sun shone down like hammered brass. The sea below was vivid turquoise and without a fleck of foam. Hour after hour passed. Around midnight the plane ran into heavy clouds and then a rain squall. There was a brief period of bumps and jolts, and then the stars could be seen again and the plane settled into a smooth flight once more. The crushing monotony returned.

Shortly after 2 A.M. Smith and Ulm received a scribbled note from Lyon reporting that he had spoken to the *S.S. Manoa* and that soon the ship would be sighted. Ulm was at the controls when the lights of the ship became visible and he circled the steamer while Smith signaled with a searchlight. The *Manoa* was no more than a black blur on the surface of the sea, but the crew of the *Southern Cross* was exhilarated by it. Any break in the tedium was like food to a starving man, and it was comforting to know that there were people roaming the Pacific like themselves.

The first glow of dawn put the crew in a brighter frame of mind. When the *Southern Cross* entered her second day of non-stop flight, there was a growing sense of elation that they were nearing their goal, or at least the first of their three goals. At 7:35 A.M., they were but 323 miles from Wheeler Field.

Now came a bewildering part of the journey. They were flying through feathery clouds, when suddenly Ulm pointed excitedly off the port bow. He scribbled on his note pad just one word, "Land!" He felt sure that he had sighted a cliff, and he shook Smith's hand in congratulations. But Ulm was wrong. It was a cloud mirage, a gray-white peak of mist, nothing more.

Then Smith sighted three dark brown bulges that he took to be rocks, and he headed the *Southern Cross* for them. But as the plane drew close, the rocks dissolved. Another mirage.

At last, it happened. At 10:52 A.M., with Smith at the controls, a dome-shape rose off the port bow. This bulge did not disappear but loomed higher and higher. It was Mauna Kea, a snow-capped extinct volcano whose peak soared 12,000-feet. The crew of the *Southern Cross* exchanged handshakes. A third of their job had been done.

Bells rang, whistles shrieked and thousands waved from the streets of Honolulu as the *Southern Cross* passed over the city, and a huge crowd was on hand to greet the ship at Wheeler Field. Their stay in Hawaii was brief. After a night's sleep, they flew on to Barking Sands, an airfield on the nearby island of Kauai for gasoline. Early the next morning, the *Southern Cross* was in the air again, with Suva now its goal.

The crew was more confident now than during the previous stage of their journey. The trip from Oakland to Wheeler Field, with the flawless functioning of the engines and radio equipment and the preciseness of their navigation, inspired them. "We'll sit down to dinner in Sydney on Sunday night," Smith chirped. No one doubted him.

After their departure from Barking Sands, the *Southern Cross* "bowled along," to use an expression of Smith's, at a ground speed of 81 knots. They kept close to the sea to conserve fuel. Visibility was good. Oil pressure and temperature readings were perfect. But there was danger ahead, and they could see it forming. The horizon became obscured by low drifting clouds. Soon the sun was blotted out. There could be no doubt about it—a storm was blowing up ahead.

The men breakfasted on coffee and sandwiches. Their spirits were good. Then Warner jotted a note to Smith that abruptly changed everyone's outlook. They had lost the radio beam. Its signal had faded away after only three hours of flight time. They had expected it to last for seven or eight hours.

But that was not the worst. Great black rain clouds now loomed ahead. The wind whipped up. There seemed no way to escape a hammering. Smith swung the plane out of one storm only to be enveloped in another. Winds charged at them from every direction, and with the wind came sheets of water. Smith knew it was too perilous to remain at low altitude for very long; so he opened up the engines and climbed, even though the maneuver meant he would be consuming precious gas at a greater speed.

Now they were flying in a deluge. The plane bucked and lurched from the stiff winds. Not until noon did they break into clear air. But the relief did not last long. Within an hour the skies were in turmoil again.

The bursts of rain were more savage now. Water began to trickle through the edges of the windshield, soaking Smith and Ulm and adding to the general cheerlessness. The angry skies brought one blessing— there was no boredom, not a single minute of it. As daylight began to wane, new peaks of clouds heaped up on the horizon—thick, dark and menacing. Again Smith put the *Southern Cross* into a climb, awakening anew the crew's fears about the gasoline supply. Ulm wrote in his log: "We see a rotten night ahead."

The cloud bank had the color of heavy coal smoke, and within it was as black as the blackest night. Rain blotted out everything. Around 8:00 P.M. the night turned more kindly. Although thick clouds below stretched to the horizon in every direction, stars blinked on from above. Then came news from Lyon to bolster their spirits. He passed up a note to the pilot's cockpit to say that they had just swept across the equator. It made them feel as if they were beginning to master these virgin skies.

There were more storms during the night; more gusts of wind that bumped and shook the plane, more torrents of rain. From Harry Lyon came a note inquiring about the gas supply. It was a question on everyone's mind. Efforts to climb above the storms or dodge them had put a severe drain on the fuel, and this was the main worry as the first streaks of dawn pierced the sky astern. The men were now feeling the strain of the savage night, and they sat limp and listless in their seats.

On the south side of the equator, the trade wind blows from the southwest. About 550-miles from the Fijis, it met the *Southern Cross* almost head on. They could feel it strike. It rushed at them with fierce gusts and increased their worry about fuel. The supply of gas was probably sufficient if they were on course, Ulm figured. But were they on course? No one knew for certain. They were flying on Lyon's dead reckoning. When the sky cleared and the sun shone, Lyon was able to take a navigation "shot" for position. It disclosed they were approximately on course, only slightly east of the direct route to Suva.

They had been in the air more than thirty hours since leaving Hawaii. Their eyes smarted from lack of sleep. The storms were behind them, but now they were assailed by a new torment—heat, tropical heat. They flung off their coats and sweaters. Smith and Ulm flew with their shirts open, letting the trade winds slap them on their bare chests. Even this brought little relief. Throughout the morning the whitehot sun beat down and the air seemed to weigh tons.

As morning melted into afternoon, all eyes strained ahead for the first glimpse of Fiji. At 1:10 P.M., a piece of land burst into view off the starboard bow. Mound-shaped, it had a greenish-brown hue. Ulm was at the controls and he abruptly swung the ship for it. The sudden change of direction jarred awake the dozing Smith. He thought the jolt meant that Ulm had fallen asleep at the controls, and he started to berate him. But when he peered ahead his anger vanished and a wide smile crossed his face. He clapped Ulm on the back. They estimated the island to be about seventy miles away. They had enough fuel for several hours. It would be child's play.

As they swept on another island appeared, and then another—scores of them. Lyon asked Ulm to take the plane down so that he could determine their precise latitude bearing with a natural horizon. Ulm nodded assent and started the plane seaward. When he was within about twenty feet of the ocean, he leveled the ship off.

Suddenly, Ulm's heart sank. He stared ahead open-mounted. The islands had disappeared. He could see nothing but an endless span of ocean. Had he been deceived by a cloud mirage? He didn't know. "What's happened? Where are the islands?" he shrieked. His words were lost in the engines' roar.

Harry Lyons noticed his friends dismay. His reaction was a hearty laugh. Lyons knew that the islands were still there. The reason that they seemed to be swallowed up in the sea was easy to explain. They were obscured by the curvature of the earth. When the *Southern Cross* cruised at an altitude of 800-feet, the islands were in clear view. But when the plane dropped down close to the ocean, the islands slipped below the horizon. "Take the plane up," Lyons signalled. Ulm did. The islands were there, and even closer. He breathed a loud sigh of relief.

At 3:45 P.M., after 34 hours, 23 minutes in the air, the *Southern Cross* swung over Suva. One more hurdle remained. There was no airfield on the island; however, a landing area had been staked out at a cricket field, the Albert Park Sports Oval, by name. It was short—fewer than 400 yards in length. Smith, his efficiency dulled by the gruelling hours in the sky, was at the controls. He put the plane into a gentle glide. Its speed was a brisk 65 m.p.h. when it touched down, and it barreled toward a thicket of trees at the end of the strip. Smith reacted instantly. He put the plane into a sudden dangerous ground loop, a sharp, uncontrollable turn. His daring gamble worked. The ship came to a dead stop without mishap.

The longest hop of the flight was over. "We have 'broken the back' of it," Smith said. The crew was certain now that they would reach Brisbane.

A frantic crowd surged about the plane as soon as the propellers stopped. A forest of waving hands and arms surrounded the fliers. The Fijians sent up loud shots of joy, but the crew of the *Southern Cross* could not hear a single one. The pound of the engines had rendered them temporarily deaf.

The crowd parted to allow the governor of Fiji and the mayor of Suva through. The governor extended a luncheon invitation and the mayor asked them all to be his guests at the Grand Pacific Hotel. The four nodded politely without quite knowing what they were agreeing to. They were a pathetic looking group—oil-stained, unshaven and genuinely dazed. Harry Lyon seemed to realize how sorry-looking they were, and he said to everyone who came near, "Excuse our appearance, sir." But after a good night's sleep and a breakfast of kippers and bacon, they began to plan the last leg of their journey.

They knew it would be foolhardy to risk taking off from the little cricket oval with a full load of gasoline. As an alternative air strip they decided upon Naselai Beach, about twenty miles to the east. Early on the afternoon of June 8, the *Southern Cross* lifted from the long, glittering strip of white sand and into the bright sky. When the plane flashed over Suva, throngs of people waved flags and handkerchiefs from the street. Then Smith turned the plane due west for Australia. "We were on the home-run," he said later. "Ahead lay the full achievement of our long-standing ambition."

Weather reports indicated that amiable skies were ahead. But by early evening Smith knew that the forecasts were wrong. The sky above turned pitch black; not a star could be seen. And threatening cloud curtains hung across the far horizon. Winds began to slap at the plane. It grew much colder. Then rain began to sprinkle upon the windshield. The worst night of the flight was about to begin.

As the wind increased, the plane bucked and lurched crazily. Smith struggled with the controls to keep the ship in the sky. All he could see was the blur of rain on the windshield. He tried to get above the chaos. The ship bucked its way to 9,000 feet but still there was no respite. Lyon and Warner, their hands numbed by the piercing cold, had to abandon making entries in the log.

Several times the plane's violent jolts almost tore Smith from his seat. He realized he could never get above the storm. Speed was his only recourse, and he opened the throttle. Lightning danced in the sky, revealing endless canyons of grim clouds with every bolt. Hour after hour the ordeal continued. Smith abandoned all attempts at navigation. His one thought was to keep the engines going. Around midnight the storm began to wane. There were more periods of blind flying in the heavy rain and thick cloud cover, but the worst was over. Not long after daybreak the dreary rain clouds fell away astern and the day turned bright and clear. It was fitting, for the greatest moment of the flight was at hand.

At first it appeared as a long gray shadow hugging the sea. Then it began to assume a distinct form. It was not a cloud. It was land—the Australian coast. Soon they could make out steep cliffs springing up from the sea and the long line of white surf. Smith and Ulm began to shout and to jab one another in the ribs with their elbows. "Loud cheers," Warner wrote in the log, "our goal is in sight."

They knew at once that they had missed Brisbane. But where were they? Then a city swept into view. Smith recognized it. It was Ballina, a town 110 miles south of Brisbane. Smith promptly headed north.

More than 15,000 wildly cheering people thronged the Eagle Farm Aerodrome in Brisbane, and when the *Southern Cross* glided down they threatened to trample the police barricades in their excitement. Smith and Ulm stepped from the cockpit and were swept from their feet and carried to a waiting limousine. Lyon and Warner were surrounded by a cheering crowd that yelled, "Good old Yanks!" They, too, were lifted from their feet. Nearly five thousand automobiles were parked near the hangars, and they blasted their horns. So loud was the din that the deafened crew could actually hear it.

The next day they took the *Southern Cross* south to Sydney, a five-hour flight. They expected a Sunday afternoon crowd of perhaps 15,000 would be on hand to greet them. When they circled the field and peered below, they were awed. A great mass of humanity covered acres on all sides of the main hangar. Officials estimated the crowd at 300,000. Later in the week, the city of Melbourne also gave the crew a thunderous reception.

The crossing of the Pacific, from the United States to Australia, was only one of Smith's many significant aviation achievements. Later in 1928, he and Ulm, with a new navigator and radioman, piloted the *Southern Cross* to the first successful crossing of the Tasman Sea, a 1,600-mile stretch of angry ocean between Australia and New Zealand. In June of 1930, Smith made a transatlantic flight, from Dublin to Harbour Grace, Newfoundland. He flew on to New York the next day, and the reception he received equalled that for Lindbergh.

In 1934, when he was thirty-five years old, Smith attempted a Pacific crossing in the "other" direction, from Australia to the United States. He had a new plane, a Lockheed *Altair*, which he dubbed the *Lady Southern Cross*. The flight was successful; indeed, he established a new speed record, and this despite near disaster on the take off from Suva. Thus Smith had scored an amazing double victory over the Pacific.

Smith made his last flight late in 1935, an attempted speed dash from London to Melbourne. He took off from Croydon and made record time to Karachi, his midway point. On November 8, he nosed the *Lady Southern Cross* almost due east across the waist of India and then over the Bay of Bengal. Something went wrong. No word was ever heard from the flight. Somewhere over the Indian Ocean, or beyond, in the steaming jungles of Burma, Smith's plane tumbled from the sky. Eighteen months later, on June 1, 1937, a Burmese fisherman retrieved a wheel that had been floating just offshore. It was from the *Lady Southern Cross*.

Smith realized his dream to fly the Pacific, and more fully than he ever could have anticipated. The New York *Times* put it best. "Sir Charles Kingsford-Smith has so many firsts to his credit that no poet could repeat the mistake that Keats made in allowing 'stout Cortez' to stare first upon the Pacific. The name Kingsford-Smith will always be first for the Pacific, whatever flying records are later made crossing it."

CHAPTER 9
LADY LINDY

Women have played a significant role in the conquest of the air since the time of the first woman aeronaut, Marie Tible. In 1784, Mademoiselle Tible persuaded a balloonist to allow her to make an ascent. When the day arrived, she wore her finest clothes—a lace trimmed dress, dainty shoes, gloves and a plumed hat.

A huge throng watched as she stepped daintily into the circular wicker walkway around the open mouth of the balloon. She waved gaily to the crowd as men holding the ropes released them and the balloon sailed aloft. Men cheered but many women were seen to weep. Mademoiselle Tible was in the air for about a half an hour and her flight covered eight miles. After she landed, she said that the air aloft was uncomfortably cold and she had experienced a ringing sensation in her ears. She declared, however, she would be willing to go up again.

Since the days of balloonists like Mademoiselle Tible, women have served as pilots of gliders and airplanes— every type of heavier-than-air craft. Women fliers have been racers and record-setters. A legion of them made a considerable contribution during World War II as members of the WAAF (Women's Auxiliary Air Force) and WASP (Women's Air Force Service Pilots).

Amy Johnson, Ruth Nichols, Jacqueline Cochran, Anne Lindbergh and Jacqueline Auriol are some of the women who carved out glittering careers in aviation. Another was Amelia Earhart. A slim girl with a boyish

figure and gray-blue wide set eyes. She won more acclaim than any other woman pilot. Her most notable feat was her non-stop flight across the Atlantic Ocean in 1932.

Amelia was born in Atchison, Kansas, in 1898. Even as a youngster she loved adventuring. She and her sister Muriel explored all the dank caves along the Missouri River near their home. Young Amelia was a fearless rider and could handle a horse Western style, with or without a saddle. She could throw a baseball as far as almost any boy and outhit most, too.

Amelia's father was a lawyer for the Rock Island Railroad and the family moved about a great deal. In one four year period, she attended six high schools. After graduation she attended Ogontz School for Girls near Philadelphia. She was always a sensitive girl. During the Christmas holidays of her senior year at Ogontz, she and her mother visited her sister, who was a student at St. Margaret's College in Toronto. This was during World War I, and Amelia was so saddened by the many crippled soldiers she saw on the streets of Toronto that she enlisted as a Red Cross nurse's aide at one of the local hospitals and did not return to college.

Always restless, she next entered Columbia University as a pre-medical student. She stayed a year then left to join her parents in California.

One Sunday she and her father drove to Long Beach to see an air meet. When Amelia saw a young man in a flying uniform, she said to her father, "Ask him how long it takes to learn how to fly."

Her father investigated. "It differs with various people," he said. "But the average seems to be about five or ten hours."

"And how much does it cost to learn?" Amelia asked.

"As much as a thousand dollars," her father answered. "Why do you want to know?"

"I'm not quite sure," said Amelia. "But I feel I've got to try it."

Not long after, Amelia took a streetcar out to Rogers Airport, a dusty open field amidst the oil wells off Wilshire Boulevard in Los Angeles. There she saw a young man tinkering with the engine of his plane. She walked over to him and announced boldly, "I want to go for a ride."

The young man grinned. His name was Frank Hawks. Within a few years he was to hold more aviation speed records than any other pilot in the world. Hawks explained the plane's instrumentation to Amelia, then helped her into the rear cockpit. Hawks climbed into the pilot's seat. A mechanic spun the propeller, and Hawks sent the plane chugging over the bumpy field and into the air.

"As soon as we left the ground," Amelia was to say later "I knew I had to fly myself."

Amelia signed up for lessons and got a job at the telephone company to pay for them. She worked all week and then spent Saturdays and Sundays at the airfield. Before long she soloed.

Her mother helped her to buy a secondhand plane, a bright yellow Kinner *Canary*. One day she took the light, modestly powered plane to 14,000-feet, establishing a new altitude record for women. It was her first official flying record.

In 1928, Amelia became a social worker at Denison House, a settlement house in Boston. She enjoyed the work but lamented the fact that she had little time for flying. One afternoon at Denison House she received a telephone call from a stranger who gave his name as Captain H. Railey. He asked Amelia if she would be interested in doing something for aviation. The wealthy Mrs. Frederick Guest wanted the first transatlantic flight by a woman to be made by an American girl. Would Amelia want to be that girl? Captain Railey wanted to know. Amelia answered that she would without a second's hesitation.

She was not actually to fly the plane but be a mere passenger. Veteran pilot Bill Stultz was to be the man at the controls; Lou Gordon was to go along as mechanic. Mrs. Guest had purchased a tri-motored Fokker for the flight. Called the *Friendship*, the plane took off from Trepassy, Newfoundland, in mid-June of 1928. From almost the first minute they were airborne, the flight was dogged by fog, rain and heavy winds. Amelia, who had hoped she would be able to fly the plane over at least a small part of the journey, had to sit and watch the skilled Stultz because she had not been trained to fly on instruments alone. Twenty hours and forty minutes after take off, the pontoon-equipped *Friendship* landed in St. George's Channel just off Burry Port, Wales.

Amelia, to her astonishment, became an immediate celebrity. She was honored and entertained on both sides of the Atlantic, and treated to a tickertape parade in New York City. Medals were showered upon her. Amelia protested. "It was Stultz who flew the plane and Gordon who got it in shape to fly," Amelia declared. "I was actually just a cuckoo in a nest. Why do people make such a fuss over me?" Nevertheless, the flight in *Friendship* marked the launching of Amelia's career.

She wrote a successful book about the crossing and became aviation editor of *Cosmopolitan Magazine*. She also worked to get more flying experience. She became a vice president of a fledgling airline and in 1931, she married George Palmer Putnam, a noted American book publisher.

On an April Sunday in 1932, Amelia quietly announced to her husband, "I'm ready to fly the Atlantic *alone*." It was a long time before he answered, Then he said, "You can make it. I'll help."

She asked Bernt Balchen, an outstanding pilot of the day, for advice and assistance, specifically to help get her Lockheed *Vega* into shape.

"What do you think about it, Bernt?" Amelia asked. "Is the plane up to it? Am I? I'll leave it up to you. If you say that one or the other isn't up to it, I'll give up."

"Of course you're up to it," Balchen answered. "I'll bet on you. As for the ship—with a little working over, she'll be equal to it." Bernt began by having the plane's body strengthened. New instruments and a new motor were installed. Extra fuel tanks were put on the wings and in the cabin.

Amelia pledged both her husband and Bernt to secrecy. She wanted no newspaper reporters poking around, giving the venture unwanted publicity that could upset her plans. If anything went wrong, she wanted to be able to abandon the idea without having the charge of "publicity stunt" hurled at her. Women flyers of the day were often targets of such a charge. Amelia said that she flew and dared dangerous missions "for the fun of it"—and it was true, but who would believe it?

By the middle of May, the plane was ready and the weather reports were good. Amelia decided upon a northern route, and selected Harbour Grace, Newfoundland, as her taking off point. Amelia, Bernt Balchen, and Eddie Gorski her mechanic, arrived at Harbour Grace on May 20, 1932. Amelia napped while Balchen and Gorski tuned the plane. Telegrams arrived from New York reporting that weather conditions, while not perfect, were favorable. Balchen sent a message to Amelia's room. All it said was "Ready."

Amelia came out on the field tucking strands of unruly hair under her leather flying helmet. She wore tailored brown jodhpurs, a white silk blouse and a brown leather flying jacket. She tied a tan scarf about her throat and put a toothbrush and a comb—her only luggage—into a pocket. Her food supply was a small thermos jug of soup and a can of tomato juice.

Amelia shook hands with Balchen and Gorski and then climbed into the cockpit of the red and gold plane. A brisk wind whipped over the runway. She waved to the two men and then opened the throttle. The plane rolled smoothly ahead and lifted into the air effortlessly. Amelia held the ship close to the earth until it picked up flying speed. Then she banked in a wide turn over the town and sped across the deep blue waters of the bay. Balchen and Gorski watched intently. The engine's roar quickly faded and the plane became a mere speck in the twilight sky, then disappeared.

At first all went well. Amelia flew over great fields of snowy white clouds. The lingering sun tinted them pink. After darkness fell, the moon turned them silver.

She scanned her instrument panel. What she saw sent a chill down her spine. Her altimeter had failed. Its needle was swinging meaninglessly back and forth. It was not a great problem so long as the sky remained clear, for she would be able to see the ocean below by moonlight. But if fog or thick storm clouds came she would be in trouble.

Luck was not with her. The moon went behind a great black mountain of clouds. A storm was blowing up. Wind shook the plane and it dipped and swayed like a paper kite. Jagged streaks of lightning filled the sky. Normally she would have flown under the storm, but without an altimeter there was the chance that she would plunge into a watery grave.

One thought now gripped her mind—to climb above the clouds. The plane ascended slowly. The temperature dropped as the ship went higher. In the brilliance of a naked bolt of lightning, Amelia saw to her horror that the wings had become coated with ice. Suddenly the heavy load of ice pulled the plane into a spin. Downward it hurtled.

Amelia fought to right the plane with every ounce of her flying skill. The warmer air of the lower altitudes melted the ice, but still the plane spun downward. She gained control at last. When she leveled off she was so low that she could see the crests of white foam despite the blackness of the night.

Afterward a wonderful sense of relief swept over her. The storm quieted, the sky began to clear, and she saw one very bright star lighting the clouds. She thought it to be the loveliest sight she had ever seen in her life.

The tranquillity did not last long. Suddenly an angry streak of orange flame burst from a break in the engine manifold. It burned unceasingly, like the flame from a blowtorch. Amelia sat tense and helpless. Would it burn through its iron prison? Or was the metal strong enough to hold it in check?

Now Amelia made a bold decision. If she turned back, land was only six hundred miles away, while more than fourteen hundred miles of black ocean lay ahead. She decided to go on.

Daylight came at last. The flames spurting from the cracked manifold were not so terrifying as they had been during the night. Her spirits rose. She had forgotten about food, but she sipped some tomato juice.

Now Amelia made a new discovery. Her gas gauge had stopped working, and she had no way of judging how much fuel she had left.

The hours dragged on. The menacing flame continued to spew from the engine. She realized that her gas supply was very low. But how low? She had no way of telling.

Her only object was to find land as soon as possible. Her original destination was England, but now she changed course and headed due east for Ireland.

She strained her eyes, searching for a glimpse of land with no success. But then, gradually a great shadow seemed to be taking shape. It could be just a cloud, or perhaps mountains. But it *was* the coast of Ireland. A wave of relief flooded over her.

She dropped down for a look. It was too rocky for her to land. She saw a twisting line of glistening railroad track and followed it, believing it would lead to an airport. She found none. And now the engine was beginning to make ominous noises. She could wait no longer, she decided. She circled low. Grazing cows lifted their heads in surprise. She put the plane down gently in a green Irish pasture.

As the plane rolled to a halt, a farm hand came running toward her. Amelia climbed from the plane. "I've come from America," she said.

The farmhand removed his cap and scratched his head. Who is this, he thought—a practical joker or maybe a crazy person. He could not even tell whether it was a young boy or girl, with slim hips and short, tousled hair.

Then the owner of the farm, James Gallagher, came running up. Amelia repeated her startling piece of news.

"But who was with you?" asked the astonished farmer. "Who flew the plane?"

"I came alone," Amelia answered. "I flew the plane myself."

The farmer could only stare open-mouthed.

"Could I use your telephone?" Amelia asked. "I want to tell my husband I've landed safely."

"I have no phone," the farmer said, "but I'll drive you to Londonderry. It's only six miles."

In becoming the first woman to span the Atlantic solo, Amelia had flown the 2,026 miles in 14 hours and 56 minutes, thus eclipsing all existing speed records for the distance. The reception she received in America rivaled that of Lindbergh in its fervor. The press took to calling her "Lady Lindy." The United States Government awarded her the Distinguished Flying Cross and several other nations presented her with awards and medals.

While the flight ranks as her greatest triumph, it was not her last success. Only a few weeks after her return to the United States, she dashed from coast to coast in nineteen hours, fifteen minutes to break the women's speed record. In 1935, she became the first woman to fly the Pacific from west to east, from Hawaii to Oakland.

Having crossed the Atlantic and a wide span of the Pacific, Amelia's next goal was to fly around the world, becoming the first woman to do so. She planned to follow a route close to the equator, and thus become the first person of either sex to make the trip by the longest route. Her plane was to be a twin-engine Lockheed *Electra*, one of the first all-metal air liners. The passenger seats were removed to make room for additional fuel tanks.

Naturally, she wanted to make the flight alone. But the vastness of the Pacific Ocean, together with the smallness of the islands she was to touch, convinced her to take a navigator. She chose Harry Manning, a ship's captain and a personal friend. They took off in March 1937, heading west. On attempting a take off from Hawaii, the plane cracked up. Amelia and Captain Manning were not injured, but they had to bring the plane back to the mainland for repairs.

In May, when the flight was finally rescheduled, Amelia had to find a replacement for Captain Manning who was no longer available. She chose Fred Noonan, an experienced over-the-water navigator. Some of Amelia's friends did not have the faith in Noonan that she had, however.

Wind and weather conditions were now such that it was more practical to make the flight in an easterly direction, even though this meant that the most arduous part of the trip—the crossing of the Pacific—would come last. The first leg of the flight was uneventful. They crossed the Atlantic, then Africa and continued eastward to Australia.

They flew on to Lae, New Guinea. Amelia was exhausted when they arrived. Yet the most difficult part of the trip was ahead. "I shall be glad when we have the hazards of navigation behind us," she wrote in her logbook.

The next stop was to be Howland Island, a tiny speck of sun-broiled coral. Two miles long and less than a mile wide, it lay 2,556 miles to the east. For the first 500 miles of the flight, Amelia was to be guided by radio signals from New Guinea. The U.S. Coast Guard stationed the cutter *Itasca* at Howland to send radio signals over the final 500 miles of the flight, but this still left 1,500 miles of ocean over which there would be no radio contact, no landmarks—nothing. Shortly before leaving Lae, Noonan discovered that the radio was not working properly. Even so, they decided to take off as planned.

The radio operators aboard the *Itasca* kept close watch on the time, and began sending signals even before they thought Amelia was actually within radio range. At 2:45 A.M. on July 2, the *Itasca* established contact with the flight. There was loud static that prevented most of the message from getting through, but radiomen thought that they heard the phrase "cloudy and overcast." Several attempts were made to talk with Amelia and Noonan, but there was no indication that either one received the messages, nor was there any acknowledgment of the weather reports that the *Itasca* was sending on the hour and half-hour.

At 6:15 A.M., the *Itasca* heard Amelia report that she estimated her position to be about 200 miles from Howland. She asked for her bearings, then whistled into her microphone to give the *Itasca* radiomen a signal for a fix. But the clatter of static was so great, it blotted out her signal.

When the men on the *Itasca* next heard Amelia, her voice had an anxious pitch, "Please take a bearing on us and report in half an hour," she pleaded. Again she whistled into her microphone, but again the signal was useless.

At 7:42 A.M., Amelia was heard yet again. This time she was frightened. "We must be on you, but we cannot see you," she said. "Our gas in running low." Crew members of the *Itasca* lined the ship's rails and started westward into the morning sky. No plane appeared.

Radio signals continued to go out from the *Itasca*, and the ship's radiomen persisted in their attempts to establish voice contact. Finally, at 8:00 A.M., Amelia reported that she was receiving messages but not clearly enough to get a bearing. At 8:45 A.M., Amelia reported, "We are on a line of position of 157-337. . . . we are running north and south." It was Amelia's last message, and it was of no value. Without a point of reference, "157-337" was meaningless.

When no further word was heard from the flight, the men of the *Itasca* became anxious. They realized the plane had probably run out of fuel, yet they could not leave Howland to begin a search while there was the slightest chance that the flight was still in the air and trying to make contact. By noon, however, everyone realized that the *Electra* was down.

The U.S. Navy launched a search at once, but aside from the *Itasca*, there were few vessels near Howland. It took most of the search ships several days to reach the area. The *Itasca* combed the waters north of the island. During daylight hours, the ship sent up a dense smoke screen that could be seen for miles. After dark the vessel's searchlights were pointed toward the sky. The search continued for sixteen days. But the ships and planes found nothing, not even the barest sign of the downed plane. "There were eight-foot seas with fifteen-feet between the crests the day that the plane went down," said Bill Galton, the radio operator aboard the *Itasca* who heard Amelia's last verified words. "I figure her plane went down and broke up somewhere near Howland."

In the years that followed, Amelia's fate was often the subject of rumor. At the time of her flight, Japan was fortifying her island posses-sions in the Pacific, and there were persistent stories that Amelia and Noonan had been taken prisoner by the Japanese in the Marianas, an island group north of New Guinea. No conclusive evidence was ever offered as to what happened, however. The disappearance of Amelia Earhart has remained one of aviation's most durable and challenging mysteries.

CHAPTER 10
AROUND THE WORLD

The date: June 23, 1931. The place: Roosevelt Field, Mineola, Long Island. The sky is overcast. Heavy mists shroud the field.

At the far end of the take off strip, Wiley Post, a short, stocky man with a trim mustache, revs up the powerful engine of a stubby monoplane. His navigator, Harold Gatty, bends over charts in the cramped cabin behind the huge fuel tank. A few minutes before five A.M., Post, cool, even impassive, guns the engine and sends the tiny ship down the soggy grass runway and into the air. Eight days, fifteen hours and fifty-one minutes later they are back, having completed a record flight around the world.

Post and Gatty were not the first to make a globe-girdling flight, but theirs was the most spectacular—by far. Four Army fliers had flown around the world in 1924. They used three planes and required seven engine changes. The flight took 175 days. The Graf Zeppelin circled the globe in 1929 in 21 days.

So the Post-Gatty flight shattered all previous records. And it did more. It served as an impressive demonstration of human courage and endurance, and of mechanical proficiency as well. Post and Gatty did not "spell" one another, that is, take turns at the controls as was frequently the case in long hops of the day. Gatty navigated—plotted the course, kept a check on fuel, and watched for airfields. Post flew. They showed amazing fortitude in being able to withstand the hours—indeed, days—of bore-dom and fatigue.

As for their airplane, its single Pratt and Whitney Wasp engine operated flawlessly and required no maintenance in face of raging seas, towering mountains and howling wastes throughout the 15,470-mile flight. It set a new standard in reliability.

Both Post and Gatty were somewhat uncomfortable as heroes. They were modest and likeable, never cocky or flashy, qualities adopted by many fliers of the day. Post didn't even dress like an aviator. Instead of the leather jacket, jodhpurs and white silk scarf, he wore a business suit with a shirt and tie.

Although he could be reserved and reticent, Post had a quick smile and was usually easy to approach and easy to talk to, especially when the subject was flying. Post was born near Grand Saline, Texas, in 1899, and flying was almost always the dominant thing in his life.

School never interested him. He dropped out when he was fourteen years old. Not long after, a county fair was held at Lawton, Oklahoma, about fifty miles from the farm where the Post family then lived. One of the attractions was an "aeroplane acsent." No one in the area had ever seen an airplane. This one was an old Curtiss pusher. When he thought no one was looking, Post climbed into the plane's cockpit. He got his ears boxed for the effort, but from that day on he was possessed by the idea of flying.

At sixteen, Post attended a school for automobile mechanics in Kansas City. He returned to Oklahoma to work in a garage, then on a construction gang and later as a "roughneck" with an oil drilling crew.

He fed the boilers, lugged drinking water and climbed the derricks to thread steel cables through the pulleys. It was dirty, tiring work.

After four years and several losing ventures in oil well speculations, Post decided to change careers. A flying circus—two planes, two pilots and a parachute jumper—came to a nearby town. Post went out to the field, told the men about his ambition to become a flyer, and asked for a job.

The head pilot shook his head. "Not a chance," he said. "You need experience to be a pilot."

Then the parachute jumper spoke up. "Let him take my place," he declared. "I'm not in shape to make the jump tomorrow."

The pilot turned to young Wiley. "How about it?" he asked. "You don't need any experience. Just nerve."

Post agreed to give it a try although he was not enthusiastic about the idea. The pilot—his name was Tibbs—agreed to pay him five dollars.

A big crowd was on hand the next afternoon. Tibbs gave Post a folded parachute and showed him how to buckle it on. The two climbed into the plane and Tibbs took it to two thousand feet. Then he cut the throttle so the prop wash would not blow his young pupil away. "O.K. Let's go," he ordered.

Post climbed from the cockpit onto the wing, then slowly edged his way out and into position. When Tibbs gave the signal, he jumped. He plunged toward the ground headfirst. It was a horrifying sensation, and Wiley thought for sure he was going to die. Then the parachute opened and he began to enjoy it.

He landed in a freshly plowed field. As he touched down, a stiff wind caught the open 'chute and jerked him off his feet. It then pulled him ignominiously and somewhat painfully over the soft earth. A handful of spectators were now upon the scene and they collapsed the parachute to save Post from further embarrassment.

Tibbs, impressed by Post's courage if not his skill, offered him fifty dollars to make another jump the following week. It went off without a hitch. Tibbs then inquired if the young daredevil would like to become his full time " 'chute man." Wiley said he would.

Post was a stunt parachutist for two years, although he remained in

Tibbs' employ for only a few weeks. He found it more profitable to free-lance. He could make as much as two hundred dollars a day, and his only expense was the thirty or forty dollars he had to pay a pilot to take him aloft. During these two years, Post learned a great deal about flying, enough to be able to solo, in fact.

Public interest in flying circuses began to wane in the mid-1920's, and Post returned to the oilfields. On his first day back at work, a splinter of metal sheared from a bolt and flew into Post's left eye. The resulting infection cost him the sight of the left eye and impaired his hearing. He was filled with deep despair at first but then his fighting spirit returned.

For the loss of his eye, Post collected $1,800 in compensation and used the money to buy his first airplane, a battered *Canuck*. He flew it for enjoyment but it also was a means of income. He hired out to flying circuses on weekends and took passengers on sightseeing jaunts. He used it to instruct would-be fliers and carried oil men out to their lease holdings and speculators to potential sites. One man Post often carried was F. C. Hall, a wealthy Oklahoman. In 1928, Post went to work for Hall as his personal pilot.

Wiley had been flying all of this time without a license. He had never taken the test because he feared the lack of sight in his left eye would cause him to fail. But after joining Hall, Post took a rigid Commerce Department examination—and passed.

In 1929, Post went to work for Lockheed Aircraft as a test pilot, and the same year he competed in the National Air Tour. He flew at a faster speed than any of the other entrants, but the handicap he had to bear because of his plane's extra power cost him the prize.

Oil man Hall hired Post as his personal pilot again in 1930, and he told Wiley to order a new Lockheed *Vega*. A stocky little monoplane, the *Vega* had a fuselage that was essentially a plywood tube, with no interior bracings, depending on its specialized construction and ribs for structural strength. The ship was painted a bright white and christened the *Winnie Mae* after Hall's daughter, Winnie Mae Fain.

Post and Hall entered the plane in 1930 National Air Race from Los Angeles to Chicago. In the weeks before the race, Wiley had the plane's wing mounted at a lower angle to offset the increased air resistance of higher speeds, and he ordered additional fuel tanks installed. When he was through modifying the plane, Post believed it to be the fastest in existence.

Post then asked Harold Gatty to lay out a course for him. The slim and reticent Gatty, thirty years old, a graduate of the Royal Australian Naval College, was regarded as one of aviation's most skilled navigators. Will Rogers once said of him: "He knows the moon like a lobbyist knows senators."

Post won the race, setting a new speed record of nine hours, nine minutes and four seconds over the 1,760-mile route. So perfect was the course that Gatty plotted, that even though Post's compass broke down at the midway point, he was able to hold the plane true and beat his closest rival by thirty minutes.

The race earned Post $7,500 and national acclaim. In general, however, this was a period of national indifference toward aviation. The airplane was yet to win acceptance as a means of public transportation and this despite the fact that the United States was crisscrossed by air routes. People needed further proof of the airplane's reliability. Post asked himself how this could best be demonstrated. The Atlantic had been spanned many times. Charles Kingsford-Smith had conquered the Pacific. The two coasts of the United States had been brought to within less than thirteen hours of one another. Besides the public's lack of interest, there was a new threat—the *Graf Zeppelin* had recently completed its around-the-world flight, and the promoters of dirigibles were beginning to challenge the airplane's pre-eminence. Post weighed all of this evidence and decided he would attempt a globe-girdling flight, his goal being to demonstrate aircraft dependability. He would seek to break the *Graf Zeppelin's* speed record as well. Hall agreed to sponsor the flight.

Throughout the winter of 1930-1931, Post was kept busy making preparations. Practically the first thing he did was to enlist Gatty's services. The two men studied maps and information on terrain, landing fields and airport facilities. Gatty prepared a complete set of navigational charts based upon a course that started out and finished in New York and included these stops: Harbour Grace, Newfoundland; Chester, England; Hanover and Berlin, Germany; Moscow, Novosibirsk, Irkutsk, Blagoveshchensk and Khabarovsk, Russia; Solomon and Fairbanks, Alaska; Edmonton, Canada; and Cleveland, Ohio.

Extra fuel tanks were installed. Those in the plane's "high wing" held 241 gallons, while those that had been installed in the fuselage had a capacity of 299 gallons. The robust nine-cylinder air-cooled Wasp engine was fitted with a supercharger, enabling it to develop 420 horsepower at 2,000 r.p.m. The plane could cruise at 150-190 m.p.h., depending upon its altitude and fuel load. Post and Gatty figured that the plane would consume about 22 gallons of fuel an hour. Allowing for some loss of speed because of contrary winds, they worked out a flight schedule that had them arriving back in New York after eight days, certainly no more than nine days. Their timetable proved remarkably accurate.

Post realized that during the trip there would be no fixed routine in eating and sleeping. Thus, he sought to break out of his normal routine before the departure. He never allowed himself to sleep during the same hours in any two days of the same week. He found that by limiting his diet he could get along on much less sleep.

A few weeks before the flight was to take place, Post and Gatty took the *Winnie Mae* to Washington and called upon diplomatic representatives of the countries they planned to visit or fly over in order to obtain the necessary clearances. The United States did not have diplomatic relations with the Soviet Union at the time, but the fliers were able to complete arrangements with Russia through the Amtorg Trading Corporation. On May 23, 1931, they arrived at Roosevelt Field. Six months of preparation were behind them; they were ready to go.

Bad weather kept the *Winnie Mae* on the ground for almost a full month. Despite the wait and the increasing tension, Post remained undisturbed. The weather reports were finally favorable and the moment for take off arrived. Post gave the plane a final inspection and posed courteously for photographers. When he revved up the engine and headed the plane down the runway, his face showed no sign of worry or strain. It was almost as if he were making a hop to Newark.

For Gatty, the trip was more of an adventure, and he felt a little nervous. Even so, his first logbook entry was terse and professional. "Took off, 4:55 Daylight Saving Time; set course 63°," was all it said.

Six hours and forty-seven minutes later, the *Winnie Mae* landed at Harbor Grace, Newfoundland. The fliers had a meal; the plane was refueled, and then they departed on the long transatlantic hop. There were forecasts of "dirty weather" and they were accurate. Storms and turbulence hammered the *Winnie Mae* most of the way. Although Gatty was later to remark that he was tossed about "like a dice in a box," his logbook entries were unemotional. "Cloudy," he wrote. "Strong following wind," was another entry. When the weather was at its worst, "Flying blind," was all he put down. Twenty minutes later, this was followed by the observation, "Ditto." And three hours later he wrote a second "Ditto."

Gatty's brevity was in keeping with his character, but it is also a fact that he had little time to write. Because of the curvature of the earth, the plane's course required constant changes in direction and altitude. Gatty had to make observations every half an hour. He used three instruments: a sextant, a drift indicator and ground speed indicator. He carried three chronometers to make sure he would always have accurate time. He had an elaborate radio set but was kept so busy he seldom had time to send out signals. It was aboard in case of an emergency. A big fuel tank separated Gatty from Post and the cockpit, and the two men communicated through a speaking tube.

Despite the bad weather and the buffeting they received over the Atlantic, Post was his unruffled self when they landed at Chester, England. Less than two hours later, they were in the air again. They crossed the North Sea, and then picked up the Rhine River. They set down at Hanover to get exact bearings to Tempelhof Airdrome near Berlin.

Post hoped to get some sleep in Berlin, but the mass of enthusiastic Germans who greeted the plane put a crimp in his plans. They hoisted Post and Gatty to their shoulders and paraded them about. Then there were radio interviews. After a hearty meal, the fliers finally got to bed. When they were awakened the next morning, they were told that they had set a transatlantic speed record, breaking the mark established by Alcock and Brown a decade before. Their trip was only one-quarter complete, but already it had achieved renown.

They left Berlin before dawn the next morning. More bad weather dogged the flight to Moscow. They were met by a small but enthusiastic band of Russians at October Field. That night there was a banquet, and the Russians drank vodka, smoked and talked. Post and Gatty wound up with only two hour's sleep. Yet Post was buoyant; they were only three days out of New York and already close to the halfway mark.

When they arrived at the airport, Post's confidence quickly melted. A serious error had been made in filling the fuel tanks, and the *Winnie Mae* was so overloaded Post doubted he could get the plane off the ground. Post had given careful instructions as to the number of gallons to be loaded; but he overlooked the fact that the Russian measure added twenty percent to the American gallon. Airport officials would not allow Post to bleed out the extra fuel onto the ground. It had to be siphoned out, a laborious, time-consuming job. Post and Gatty fretted. They had planned to take off before daybreak, but the sun was high in the sky before the *Winnie Mae* finally lifted from the runway and headed for Novosibirsk, more than 1,700 miles to the east.

Post opened the throttle wide in an effort to make up for lost time. Soon they were crossing the Ural Mountains. To Gatty, they were a disappointment. The peaks—at least where they crossed—were not high; there was nothing awesome about them. The terrain was very rugged, however, with thick forests and rocky cliffs. They reached Chelyabinsk on the eastern slope of the Urals, then followed a rail line to Omsk, the largest city on this leg of the flight.

The officials who were waiting for them at Novosibirsk airport checked their passports and then whisked them to a primitive lodging house. The beds were mere wooden frames without linen bedsheets. There was no running water. They were about to try to get some sleep when their host burst into the room. In halting English he got them to understand that a banquet had been arranged in their honor. It was a magnificent affair, with an enormous array of food, but it served to cut the fliers' sleep to three hours.

The next stopover was Irkutsk, a Siberian town about 900 miles away. On the last stage of the hop, Post picked up a railroad line he could follow, and Gatty was able to put aside his instruments and get some snatches of sleep. When they landed at Irkutsk, the largest crowd they had seen since leaving Berlin was on hand to greet them.

Departing from Irkutsk, they flew over the eastern shore of Lake

Baykal, over the high Yablonovy Mountains, and the flat, grassy plains beyond. When they reached Blagoveshchensk on the Manchurian border, it was raining hard. They could not find the landing field and they were running low on fuel. Then Post spotted an open area with what looked to be runway lights. A closer inspection revealed it to be the field but it was covered with water. "This is going to be rough," Post yelled to his partner. "Hang on."

A heavy spray of water shot into the air when they glided down. The wheels sunk into thick mud and the plane jolted to a stop.

As soon as Post cut the engine, the two men jumped down to inspect their plight. It didn't take much looking around to see that they were in serious trouble. The entire field was covered with water and the black ooze beneath was from six to twelve inches deep. They had visions of their adventure ending in this remote Siberian mudhole.

A band of boot-clad Russians came toward them through the mist and rain and offered aid. But there was nothing that could be done until the weather cleared. Post and Gatty were not completely downcast. They needed sleep desperately and this was a chance to get some. When they awoke, the sky was clear and a stiff wind was blowing. With the help of a small army of Russians, they got the plane free. Then it was on to Khabarovsk, a mere 363 miles to the east. They landed at 1:30 A.M., New York time, on Sunday, June 28. They had come 8,800 miles.

The *Winnie Mae* was refueled, but the weather was so bad that they had to delay their departure until very early the next morning. The next stop was Solomon, Alaska, just east of Nome, a flight of 2,400 miles. Over the Sea of Okhostsk, they ran into the worst rainstorm that Post had ever seen. He said it reminded him of the story of the pilot who was flying an amphibian through rain so heavy that "he pulled up the wheels and landed right there—at 6,000 feet."

The sun was shining brightly when they crossed the Bering Sea. They swung over Cape Kukaliak on St. Lawrence Island, the first American territory they had seen since Bar Harbor, Maine. Fog closed in soon after. Post dropped low to try to get beneath the fog layer, only to be startled by the sight of towering icebergs. Back up into the fog he went.

They landed at Solomon early in the afternoon of June 29 after a flight of almost seventeen hours. But they did not stop to rest. Instead, they decided to refuel as quickly as possible and get as far as Fairbanks before nightfall. As Post taxied along the take off strip, he felt the plane start to sink in the mushy sand. He jammed the throttle forward to pull out, but all he succeeded in doing was sending the tail high into the air. Instantly Post hit the emergency switch. But the damage had been done. When the nose went down, the metal propeller struck the ground, bending both tips.

With a wrench, a hammer and a big, round stone, Post managed to somewhat undo the damage. The spell of bad luck had not ended, however. Gatty was swinging the propeller to restart the engine, when the motor backfired, causing the prop to spin in the opposite direction. It struck Gatty on the shoulder. "He dropped like a log," Post said.

Gatty was unconscious for several minutes, but as soon as he regained his senses he climbed aboard. Post put the ship in the air and headed for Fairbanks. They arrived there less than three hours later. The damaged prop was replaced with a new one, and the ship was refueled. Post felt the worst was over; he could feel the tension lessening.

It was raining when the *Winnie Mae* lifted into the air at Fairbanks, and it was still raining at Edmonton, 1,450 miles to the south and east, when they landed ten hours later. The field was water-soaked. Post peered down. "We should have had this crate fitted with floats," he said.

"Let's hope it's not another Blagoveshchensk!" exclaimed Gatty.

There was solid turf beneath the water and the landing was no problem, but there was no thought of trying to take off with a heavy load of gasoline. An air mail pilot at the field had a suggestion. "Use the main street of town," he said. "It's wide; it's concrete. You'll have no trouble."

The city fathers were happy to cooperate. They closed off the street to traffic and took down the telephone wires. Once airborne, Post and Gatty looked ahead eagerly to the final dash. The *Winnie Mae* was as nimble as ever. "It'll be as easy as a training flight," said Post.

The sun shone as they crossed Canada's vast prairies and the stretches of thick forests and blue lakes beyond. Still following a southeastern course, they headed over Lake Superior and crossed into the United States near Bessemer Junction, Michigan. They passed over the north-eastern tip of Wisconsin, then Lake Michigan, then Michigan—Flint, Pontiac and Detroit. They stopped in Cleveland for fuel and were in the air again in less than twenty-nine minutes.

The final hop was easy. It was growing dark by the time they reached the foothills of the Alleghenys, but a string of air mail beacons guided them the rest of the way. They raced across the northern tip of New Jersey and then in the distance Post could see the New York City skyline. "We had to go all the way around the world to glimpse it from the west," he thought. They landed at 8:47 P.M.

The fliers received a triumphant welcome. A fleet of planes buzzed in the sky. On the ground were crowds, microphones, photographers and reporters. The elapsed time of the journey was eight days, fifteen hours and fifty one minutes; their actual flying time was four days, twelve hours and six minutes.

Post and Gatty were not soon forgotten. Indeed, they won a secure place in aviation history, Post for his skillful piloting, and Gatty for his wizardry as a navigator, and both for their superhuman endurance.

Post's name was often in the headlines in the years that followed. In 1933, he made a solo flight around the world to establish a new record of 15,596 miles in seven days, nineteen hours and forty-nine minutes. He next tried high altitude flying. In a "Man from Mars" flying suit which he designed, he claimed a record of 49,000 feet, but a faulty barograph prevented it from being regarded as official.

His final adventure came in 1935. Accompanied by the famous comedian Will Rogers, Post set out to circumnavigate the world the "wrong" way, from east to west. They were to follow a course across Alaska and into Russia. On August 12, 1935, not far from Point Barrow, Post lifted the pontoon-equipped plane from the surface of a small lake. He had to make a steep climb to avoid a small hill. The plane stalled and went into a spin. Both Post and Rogers were dead when the Eskimo search party found them. Gatty outlived Post by 22 years. He died in 1957 in the South Pacific of a heart attack.

CHAPTER 11 POLAR PIONEER

In June 1930, rugged Bernt Balchen returned to the United States and the celebrations that had been arranged to honor his triumphant flight over the South Pole. New York City was the first stop. "Damn you," Bernt Balchen," said Mayor Jimmy Walker, fighting to hold back a smile, "all I ever do is greet you here on the steps of City Hall."

Indeed, it was true. Honor piled upon honor for Bernt Balchen, one of aviation's most heroic personalities.

Balchen had no equal as a polar flyer. A veritable iron man, he learned how to pilot an airplane in 1920 at the age of 21. His training ground was the ice, snow and cragged fjords of his native Norway. Intense and quiet spoken, his goal was always to master the forces that balked less hardy adventurers.

And he *did* master them. By the time he was 30, Bernt had taken part in polar expeditions with three of the most noted explorers of the day—Lincoln Ellsworth, Roald Amundsen and Richard E. Byrd.

Bernt was extremely knowledgeable in the mechanical aspects of aircraft, one of aviation's first experts in multi-engined aircraft. But his indomitable spirit was his greatest gift. Bernt once invited Jimmy Doolittle, who was later to gain fame in World War II, to inspect an aircraft that he was testing for a polar flight. Doolittle looked it over carefully and noticed that it was not possible to divert the heat from the exhaust stacks to the

pilot's cockpit; it could only be diverted to the carburetor. Bernt smiled at Doolittle's discovery. "The carburetor may incline to freeze," he said, "But I won't."

Bernt's courage and his virtuosity as a pilot were clearly demonstrated in late June of 1927, when he served as a member of the four-man crew of Commander Byrd's *America*, the tri-motored Fokker that made a transatlantic flight from Roosevelt Field, Long Island, to France. Unable to land at Paris because of thick ground fog, the plane was forced down in the Atlantic off the French coast. Bernt was at the controls. Thanks to his coolness and skill, the plane made a "ditched" safely and the men were able to inflate a rubber life raft, climb aboard and row ashore.

Although Balchen, Byrd and the other members of the *America's* crew were received with acclaim when they returned to the United States, the public quickly forgot the flight. After all; they were not the first to make a transatlantic crossing; they were not even the second.

Not long after his return, Bernt discussed the flight with Anton Fokker, the noted aircraft designer. "Well," said Fokker, "Lindbergh and Chamberlain stole the show all right." Balchen nodded in agreement.

"But," Fokker added, "there'll be other things to do."

Indeed, Bernt was already planning "other things." Byrd, America's explorer-hero of the 1930's, was about to launch an Antarctic expedition, and he had asked Bernt to head his aviation unit. Bernt accepted. A bold flight over the South Pole, something that no man had ever done, was the main feature of the assignment.

Byrd proposed that Bernt go to Norway to arrange for a vessel suitable for transporting men and supplies through the ice. Byrd knew that the sturdiest icebreakers of the day were of Norwegian design. At the same time, Bernt would seek out experienced men to staff the expedition.

Bernt's return to Norway was a memorable experience. He was received warmly everywhere, awarded special honors and presented to King Haakon at the Royal Palace. "You are doing great things for Norway," the stately monarch told Bernt. "We are proud of you."

Bernt received an invitation to visit his old friend, Roald Amundsen. Perhaps no man in the world knew more about the polar regions than Amundsen, and Bernt eagerly accepted. When he inquired about a ship, Amundsen suggested the *Samson*, a sturdy sailing vessel of 500 tons. Amundsen knew it well. It was the *Samson* that had carried him north on his first Arctic trip in 1896. Although a bit slow, the ship was solid and dependable.

Byrd's original plan was to use a tri-motored Fokker, the plane that had successfully carried him across the North Pole, but when Bernt returned to the United States, he learned that this had been changed. "We're going to have to use an American designed plane," Byrd told him. "After all, the Ford family is putting up a large part of the money for this expedition. I've decided upon a tri-motored Ford." A single-engined Fokker and a Fairchild were purchased as auxiliary planes.

One of Bernt's first tasks was to design landing skids that could bear the weight of the heavy Ford. The ship was ready in November and Bernt went to Detroit to take delivery. Then he and Floyd Bennett, who had piloted Byrd across the North Pole and was to serve as co-pilot on this expedition, headed for Flin Flon, a town near the Saskatchewan border in Manitoba province, a region of brutal cold and rugged terrain. Here they put the Ford through its paces, giving it every cold weather test they knew.

The expedition was an immense undertaking, and Byrd and Balchen spent well over a year making preparations. While two explorers—Amundsen and England's Robert Scott—had penetrated the continent to the South Pole, many mysteries remained to be solved. Byrd's 100-man party was to include biologists, geologists, meterologists, cartographers and photographers.

Supplies, enough to feed an army, had to be taken along. They included three tons of bacon, one ton of chicken, two tons of corned beef, 500 cases of eggs, 15 tons of flour, 400 pounds of cocoa and 375 pounds of tea. Besides the foodstuffs, the supplies included 25 tons of coal, 15,000 gallons of gasoline, 60,000 sheets of writing paper, five folding bathtubs, 8,840 bars of hand soap, an xylophone and a small player piano.

A vertible fleet of ships was required to transport the men and materials. In addition to the *Samson*, which was renamed the *City of New York*, Byrd purchased a fast and good sized freighter, the *Eleanor Bolling*. And there were two Norwegian whalers, the *Larsen* and the *Sir James Clark Ross*.

Bernt assembled a skilled team of pilots and technicians. Among them were Harold June, a Navy flyer; Alton Parker, a Marine flyer, and Dean Smith, a leading air mail pilot. There were several mechanics and an aerial photographer as well. The aircraft were flown to Norfolk, disassembled, the parts winterized, crated and then loaded aboard the *Larsen*. In September the ship got underway, heading through the Panama Canal, and then across the Pacific to Dunedin, New Zealand, the closest major port to the Ross Sea. Early in December they pushed off for the ice pack.

The width of the ice pack varies with the seasons. Toward the end of December, the beginning of the Antarctic summer, the ice becomes softer and some of it breaks into massive floes. During this period, a stalwart ship can safely press all the way to the inner rim of the Ross Sea. In March the Antarctic winter begins and the ice freezes solid again.

The weather out of Dunedin was bright and pleasant for several days, and then the lookouts spotted great fleets of icebergs, rather like sentinels guarding the mysterious land to the south. They passed Scott Island, a few hundred miles off the Antarctic coast. The sea grew heavy, and the huskies in their crates became restless and howled deep into the night. Within a few more days, they reached the outer edge of the pack, and began the treacherous 500-mile journey through the grinding floes. Sometimes the ice was so thick that it formed high walls on either side of the ship. At other times they sailed placidly in blue and open sea.

On Christmas Day 1928, the expedition caught its first glimpse of the sheer ice ridge that signaled the beginning of the continent and the end of the sea journey. The cliffs rose as high as 100 feet in some places. Often they were glass smooth and glistened in the sun. In other areas they were broken and jagged, marking a point where an iceberg had broken away. It was a place of brooding silence and cold, intense cold. Byrd now had to find an inlet where they could unload their supplies and set up camp, and he sent out exploration parties on skis. Within a week they established their outpost. Byrd named it *Little America.*

While the ships were being unloaded and the buildings constructed, Bernt set about making the planes airworthy. The Fairchild was first. Once it was reassembled, warm oil was poured into the engine and other working parts were heated by a blowtorch. Bernt was at the controls when the engine sputtered to life for the first time. He tested the plane's skis along the ice for a short distance. Bernt realized that this was to be the very first aircraft to take off from the Antarctic continent, and he felt the honor should go to the Marine pilot, Alton Parker. He signalled Parker to come and take the controls. Such thoughtfulness cost Bernt many laurels.

Flying in the Antarctic is much more difficult than it is anywhere else in the world, even more difficult than it is in the Arctic. Whereas the North Pole is a depression in the earth's surface, filled with water and sheeted with a thick layer of ice, the opposite end of the axis is a vast plateau region, where mountain peaks reach as high as 15,000 feet.

The plateau area is in the heart of Antarctica. The total land mass of the continent is about equal to that of the United States. Its jagged perimeter, interrupted by the immense Ross Sea on the Australian side and the Weddel Sea on the American side, is surrounded by pack ice. This zone is miles wide and many feet thick and is a major obstacle to those seeking to cross the Ross Sea, the inner shore of which lies relatively close to the Pole itself.

Terrain is not the only hazard in the Antarctic; winds and storms are two others. The Pole is in the center of a high pressure area and fierce winds blow constantly. In some regions, they *average* fifty miles an hour for months at a time. Storms—blizzards—are looked upon with dread. They strike almost without warning and the snow is like driving rain. A blizzard in the Antarctic can last ten days, even longer. The summer brings comparatively mild weather, however, and it's possible for the storms to subside for as long as a week.

Not long after his arrival, Bernt got a taste of the vicious Antarctic weather. With June as his co-pilot, and geologist Larry Gould as a passenger, Bernt took to the air in the Fokker. Their mission was to collect mineral specimens from a mountain range a few hundred miles from camp. They had not gone far when they encountered heavy fog and Bernt had to climb to 8,000 feet to get above it. When he estimated he had reached their destination, Bernt glided down through the cloud cover, found a landing spot and set the plane down. They drained the engine of oil, covered it and then set up their camp. June got the radio working and contacted *Little America* to report that all was well.

They spent most of the next day on the mountain and returned to camp just before dark. Gould was disappointed because the rock he found was granite, not some exotic mineral. Bernt awoke early the next morning to hear the wind singing at a high pitch. He knew immediately that a storm was blowing up. By mid-afternoon the wind was of gale proportions and it whipped open a side of their tent, upsetting the cook-stove and starting a small fire. Bernt's concern was with the plane which was anchored down by blocks of snow the men had piled on its skis. He and Gould made the pile higher and then hastily built a wall of snow blocks around the ship. The storm raged on and on, but the two men worked continually to reinforce the barricade. Only when the wind began to subside did they turn their attention to repairing the tent.

The worst was over, they believed, but then the storm doubled back. This time it was even worse. The wind whistled around the plane and threatened to lift the Fokker into the air. Gould and June, although lashed by the fury of the storm, each grasped a wing while Bernt sought to lash the tips to solid ice. The force of the gale was so strong that they could lean against it, just as one would lean against the side of a building.

When at last the wind subsided, the sky turned leaden and heavy snow began to fall. It snowed for two days. They were in agreement now that their project should be abandoned and they should return to *Little America* as soon as the weather permitted a take off.

Their ordeal was not over. A second blizzard was soon upon them. At its height the three men worked furiously to reinforce the barricade of snow blocks around the plane. At one point Bernt entered the cockpit. The air speed indicator was registering a wind velocity of one hundred miles an hour. Worse than that, the radio was not working.

That night it was almost impossible to keep the tent lashed down. Their sleeping bags had become damp and offered them little comfort. The following day the weather was still bad. In the dim light of morning, Gould peered out and saw that the plane had been torn from its anchorage. Although the storm still raged, Bernt hurried out to investigate. The wind had driven the plane about a half a mile from the campsite, and when Bernt came upon it, he was sickened at its sight. The plane was a wreck, beyond any hope of salvage.

The next day the storm finally blew itself out. They managed to put their radio in working order, but could only receive messages, not send them. Bernt took out a bundle of orange flags and laid out a landing strip in the snow hoping it would be spotted by a rescue plane.

Now they waited. Day after day passed. It was little comfort to listen to the radio and hear Byrd appealing to them to return. They rationed the remaining food. Bernt had no fears about the situation. He knew he could walk—ski—out; he knew he was tough enough. But he was not so sure about the others. The test never came. Toward evening of the eleventh day, the drone of an airplane's engine roused them. It was the Fairchild, piloted by Smith and Byrd. Rescue was assured.

Once back at *Little America*, Bernt and the others had little time to mull over their experience. Winter, with its long months of eerie darkness, was almost upon them. Hangars of snow blocks had to be built to protect the remaining planes, and the engines and other vital parts had to be packed in grease. On April 17, the sun set for the last time. They would not see it again until late in August.

Besides the darkness, there was the cold. The temperature was such that a person's flesh could freeze even before he knew it. But the members of the expedition were pleasantly snug. A well-ventilated, well-heated shelter had been burrowed into the snow. It consisted of two main structures—a mess hall, which was fitted with bunks, and an administration building. Both of these were constructed of insulated board and connected by tunnels to a maze of smaller rooms that had been hollowed out of the snow. The crate that had contained the fuselage of the Fairchild served as a radio shack. There was an igloo library and an igloo gymnasium, and everywhere there were caches of stores and scientific equipment.

As a safeguard against boredom and even a breakdown in morale, the men followed a rigorous daily schedule, and took turns hauling coal, washing dishes, shoveling snow, standing fire watch and making meteorological readings.

Bernt spent much of his time planning the flight to the Pole, a formidable trip, 800 miles each way. He had made flights of this distance many times, but in this case the terrain was a great peril. At a point about midway to the Pole stood the Queen Maud Mountains, a towering range that divided the glacial mass along the coast from the continent's inland plateau. Bernt knew that it would be impossible for the Ford to lift over the mountains. He would have to fly through the range, using a narrow gap cut by a glacier.

From the trials he had made in Canada, Bernt had gained an accurate idea of how the Ford would perform. He judged weight to be the critical problem. Besides fuel and the crew, food, emergency supplies including a sledge, a one-hundred pound camera and a prodigious amount of photographic equipment had to be taken along. The Ford was not capable of carrying this load 1,600 miles. A supply of fuel would have to be cached along the route. The aviation unit and Byrd spent countless hours discussing what was essential to the flight and what was not. Bernt did not believe a large stock of food was a necessity. He preferred that the weight be given over to gasoline. Events were to prove him right.

The flight was planned as the final leg of a four-stage assault. First, a sledge party—the sledges drawn by huskies—was to leave *Little America* and lay out stores of food at fifty-mile intervals over a two-hundred mile stretch. Second, a geological expedition under Gould's command would set out, following the route of the base-laying party. Third, Smith would fly to the foothills of the Queen Maud range and there deposit a supply of gasoline. This, later, was to be used on Bernt's flight, the fourth stage of the operation. Late in August, when the darkness finally ended, signalling the beginning of the Antarctic spring, the plan was put into action.

While Bernt and the mechanics worked to reactivate the aircraft, the base-laying party and, soon after, the geological party, set out. Once Smith had deposited the fuel cache and marked it properly, there was nothing to do but wait for favorable weather. On November 27, Gould radioed that his party had reached a point about one-hundred miles from the Queen Maud Mountains and that weather conditions were ideal. Bernt and Byrd conferred and agreed that the time had come. They would leave the next day.

Food, extra cans of gasoline, emergency gear and the rescue sledge were stowed in the plane during the morning hours. Then the huge, gray Ford was rolled into take off position at the end of the runway—a long, fairly level stretch of hardpacked snow. The mechanics held torches close to the long snouts of the engines, and when each one was sufficiently warmed, they hand turned long cranks that activated the starters.

Bernt was at the controls. One by one the cylinders caught and the engines roared to life. He opened the throttles wider and wider until the whole plane shook; then he throttled down and tested each engine at various speeds. He smiled with satisfaction. "They purred like three kittens," he said later.

Bernt gunned the engines. The plane lurched forward on its skis, paused for a split second, and then slipped smoothly along the snow. After it had lifted into the air, Bernt swung the ship wide and then pointed its nose south. Byrd was busy with his Bumstead compass, June was at the radio and McKinley tinkered with his cameras.

Little America quickly fell away. Ahead lay the vast ribbed expanse of the Ross shelf, a land of utter desolation. There were small clouds and some mist but now and then the crew could perceive the tracks of a dog team.

After almost four hours in the air, Bernt made out a handful of tiny dark specks in the distance. Gradually they took shape. It was the Gould party. Bernt banked the plane and McKinley released a bag that contained chocolate and cigarettes. They watched the men scurry to recover it. Then Bernt put the ship back on course.

Not long after, the foothills of the Queen Maud Mountains began to form. Soon the outline of glistening, rugged peaks filled the entire horizon. Bernt took the plane to 6,000 feet, scanning the mountains for a passage through. Glaciers, moving like great frozen rivers, had cut massive gorges in the range. Bernt spotted the one he was seeking—the Liv Glacier.

Near the mountains, the air became turbulent, filled with tricky downdrafts, and several times the controls were almost wrested from Bernt's hands. Bernt's eyes were glued on the gorge ahead. He knew he needed more altitude to get above the canyon floor. He struggled with the controls. But the Ford would not climb.

"Drop weight!" Bernt shouted. "Drop 200-pounds!" June sprang for the fuel dump-value.

"No! No!" Bernt screamed. "Not gas! Drop food!"

McKinley was the first to act. He threw open the trap door and thrust a 150-pound canvas bag of supplies earthward. It wasn't enough. The plane refused to climb.

"Drop more!" Bernt ordered. McKinley and June tumbled a 250-pound bag through the hatchway. Bernt felt the plane lift slowly, seemingly inches.

They were in the pass now, but only a few feet above the floor. Bernt knew he had to get higher. He eased the plane toward one of the walled sides of the gorge. It was strategy born of long experience. As the plane neared the wall, updrafts caught and lifted it. When the plane finally had made its way through, most of the crew members breathed a sigh of relief. Not Bernt. He let out a hearty yell.

Ahead lay the Polar plateau, a broad white tableland. It was undoubtedly the loneliest land on earth.

Bernt held the ship at 12,000 feet, about 1,000 feet above the plateau.

To his left in the distance he could see a chain of hostile mountains. These had been charted by Amundsen. But to his right, farther away, was another range. These appeared on no existing charts.

While the plateau area itself looked to be level, it actually undulated. Bernt's altimeter readings varied from 9,500 to 11,000 feet, although he kept the plane on a level course. There was mild turbulence, enough to prevent the taking of sun shots. But Byrd's calculations indicated that they were on course and approaching the bottom of the earth.

When they were about fifty miles from the Pole, dark clouds gathered. Bernt gave them a worried look. He turned the controls over to June and went aft to confer with Byrd. Storm or no storm, they decided to press on.

Not long after he had returned to the controls, Bernt received a message from Byrd. They were there! But Bernt felt no joy, no sense of elation as he looked below. It was a somber moment. "Our very purpose here seems insignificant, a symbol of man's vanity . . ." he later wrote. "The sound of our engines profanes the silence."

Byrd came up to the cockpit and gave Bernt written instructions for circling the pole. "Turn right three miles, then circle 180 degrees, fly six miles and circle back," they read. While Bernt circled, Byrd dropped a stone from Floyd Bennett's grave, a British flag in honor of Scott, and a Norwegian flag in honor of Amundsen. Bernt looked at his watch. It was 8:55 A.M. The date was November 29, 1929.

The trip home was trouble-free. The passage through the mountains, with the plane lightened as much of its gasoline was used up was not nearly so disquieting. Once through the gorge, they quickly found the orange flags that marked the fuel cache. They landed, carried the fuel aboard and were back up in the air in less than an hour.

There was wild excitement at *Little America* when Bernt set the plane down. While their numbers were few, the mechanics and others sounded like thousands. Bernt took the warm greetings in stride. When they were over, he got out his skis for a hike, explaining that he hadn't had his exercise that day.

Late in January, when the ice-pack began to break up, the expedition sailed for the United States. There were celebrations everywhere when they arrived. Bernt's highest tribute came from President Herbert Hoover who awarded him a special medal authorized by Congress.

In the years that followed, Bernt continued his private duel against the forces of nature. During World War II, he conducted perilous rescue missions on the Greenland Ice Cap as a member of the U.S. Army Air Force. Later during World War II, he served with the Office of Strategic Services in a program to aid the Norwegian underground. After the War, Alaska became Bernt's field of operation. He was named Commanding Officer of the 10th Rescue Squadron of the U.S. Air Force.

"We do it!" was also Balchen's motto. Anyone who served with him knew that he never failed to obey it.

CHAPTER 12
FIRST JET FLIGHT

"Evening—first test flight of the E-28."

This terse entry in the diary of Frank Whittle, a Royal Air Force Wing Commander, for May 15, 1941, is the only written record made by him at the time of a landmark event in aviation history—the flight of the first successful jet airplane.

Staged at an R.A.F. field at Cranwell and shrouded in the utter secrecy of wartime, the flight of the Gloster-Whittle E-28 was not revealed to the general public until January 6, 1944. On that date a joint statement by the R.A.F. and the U.S. Army Air Force disclosed that several hundred test flights had been successfully completed and that production was beginning on a new type of aircraft that was propellerless and moved by propulsive exhaust power. Planes of this design will be capable of "extreme speeds at the highest altitudes," the announcement declared.

The story of the development of the first jet craft is largely Frank Whittle's story. In 1930, at the age of 22, Whittle applied for a patent for a gas turbine jet engine. This was the beginning. There then followed eleven years of painful struggle—of engineering problems, financial difficulties, and frustrations arising out of official policy. But Whittle's zealous determination to turn his idea into a reality carried the day. Rightly, his name is today ranked along side that of James Watt, George Stephenson and Charles Parsons in the field of propulsion engineering.

Jet propulsion is a perfect illustration of one of the fundamental laws of nature—Newton's Third Law concerning action and reaction. A child's balloon is a simple model of a jet engine. Fill a balloon with air, then let it go. The balloon rushes across the room as it expels the air. This isn't difficult to explain. This "rushing out" forces an opposite reaction—the forward push. This is what sends the balloon careening across the room. Of course, the theory of jet propulsion was known for centuries before the time of Frank Whittle.

Whittle's great contribution was that he married the principle of jet propulsion with the gas turbine and applied the idea to heavier-than-air flight.

A word about the turbine, a device first patented by John Barber in 1791. A turbine is a type of engine that is driven by the pressure of steam, water or air, which is directed against the curved vanes of a wheel. Whittle often likened the turbine to a very powerful windmill. In the gas turbine jet engine, the turbine, while vital, does not provide the propulsion. The engine works like this: there are four major parts—a compressor to suck in and compress the air, a combustion chamber, the turbine, and an exhaust pipe ending in a jet nozzle.

These parts are arranged in that order in a tube-shaped structure. Air is drawn in at the front of the tube and passed through in one continuous flow. In the combustion chamber, air that has been compressed is used to burn fuel. The hot gases that result shoot out of the nozzle at the back at high speed to push the plane forward.

One other point is important: before the gases leave the engine, they rush through the curved vanes of the turbine to turn it, thereby driving the compressor.

Why bother with a jet engine anyway? The traditional piston engine had served airmen well, providing for speeds in excess of 400 m.p.h. Why change? The overriding argument is that the jet engine is a great deal simpler than the piston type; it has fewer moving parts. It is much more durable. In addition, the jet engine's efficiency increases with speed and altitude. This is why jet planes can travel so much faster and higher than piston-powered craft.

Some people contend that Germany was the first country to develop and test fly a jet aircraft, and this argument is not without some merit. It is a well known fact that the Heinkel firm in Germany built a jet-powered airplane that was test flown at Rostock on August 27, 1939, nearly two years before the E.28's flight at Cranwell. Heinkel called their plane the He-178, and it flew at a speed of 435 m.p.h.

Italian engineers also developed an early jet craft. On November 30, 1941, Commandant Mario de Barnardini piloted a Caproni-Campini jet airplane from Turin to Rome, a distance of about 300-miles, in record time. However, this project, like the German one, was abandoned before any production planes were turned out.

On the other hand, the Whittle project bore fruit. Whittle's jet engines were used to power the Gloster "Meteor," the only service jet plane used by the Allies in World War II. Great Britain's great surge in the field of jet aviation after World War II was founded on engines modeled after those developed by Whittle. That's not all. In the United States, a pair of engines based upon Whittle's specifications and calculations were used to power America's first jet aircraft, the Bell XP59A "Airacomet," which took to the sky for test flights late in 1942. At almost exactly the same time, Germany successfully flew its Messerschmidt Me-262, which saw service as a bomber in 1944.

Frank Whittle was born on June 1, 1907, in Coventry, the first child of hard-working parents. He inherited his engineering skills from his father, who, although never schooled as an engineer, was an expert mechanic and a clever inventor. When Frank was nine, the family moved to Leamington Spa where his father opened a small machine shop. Before he had reached his teens, young Frank knew how to drill a valve stem and was a skilled lathe hand.

At school Frank was less than an enthusiastic pupil, but in his leisure time he read avidly, devouring books on astronomy, physiology and engineering, particularly aircraft engineering. It was during this period that he first became interested in turbines.

In 1923, Frank was accepted into the Royal Air Force as an aircraft apprentice, and began the training that was to serve him so well in later years. He was first schooled in aircraft assembly, dividing his day between the classroom and the workshop. He took to the trade with such facility that at the end of his three-year apprenticeship, he was awarded a scholarship at the RAF college at Cranwell to be trained as a Flight Cadet. He graduated in July 1928, ranking second in his class. Whittle was then assigned to a fighter squadron that formed part of what was known as the "Air Defense of Great Britain."

Many aeronautical engineers of the day were searching for the type of power plant that could provide a high altitude, high speed aircraft. Whittle felt that the solution lay with jet propulsion, but with the driving engine of the conventional piston type. Then one day he hit upon the plan of using a turbine engine in place of piston power. "Once the idea had taken shape," he once said, "it seemed rather odd that I had taken so long to arrive at a concept which had become very obvious and of extraordinary simplicity."

Whittle explained the engine's principle to his instructors at the RAF flight school he was then attending, and then to the school's commandant. Eventually, he was invited to present his sketches and calculations to the Air Ministry. The result was disappointing. Officials of the Air Ministry said that his scheme was not practical, that materials did not exist that were capable of withstanding the tremendous stresses and high temperatures the gas turbine would generate.

But Whittle was far from discouraged. Early in 1930, he applied for and was granted a patent on the turbojet engine, and he continued working to improve and embellish his idea.

After his patent had been granted, Whittle continued in his attempts to arouse commercial interest in the turbojet. But aeronautical engineers of the day, like the Air Ministry, said that the technology did not exist to build such an engine. Also, in those years of depression, money was lacking for extravagant schemes of the type Whittle proposed.

By 1935, Whittle had about given up hope of ever seeing his plans transformed into practical shape. That year his patent came up for renewal. A fee of 15 pounds was required. Whittle was married by then and his young family was causing him considerable expense. He decided the renewal fee was a luxury he could not afford, and he let the patent lapse.

Soon after, Whittle's fortunes began to change. He filed new patents that outlined improvements to his original plan, and undertook serious negotiations to start an investment company to finance his project. In 1936, a company called Power Jets Limited was formed, its mission to produce an experimental jet engine. The actual construction of the engine was sub-contracted to the British Thompson-Houston Company, and combustion tests began at the B T-H factory in Rugby in the summer of 1936.

The Power Jets organization had no excess of money and early operations were somewhat primitive. The combustion test apparatus was built in the open, protected only by the turbine planning office which was constructed overhead. This arrangement made for some vexing problems. Deafening noise was produced whenever a combustion test was conducted, and great dense clouds of smelly smoke and vapor billowed into the planning office. There was so much vibration that once when the office staff returned from lunch, they found every desk swept clear of pens, papers, books, instruments—everything.

Despite such inconveniences, the manufacture of the first engine was well advanced by the end of the first year. In April 1937, a test run was tried. It revealed that the combustion problem had not been entirely solved, and that the compressor did not operate with the necessary efficiency. Major improvements were needed.

Other problems bore down on Whittle. A financial crisis loomed, one that was not eased until much later when the Air Ministry agreed to contribute public funds for the cause. And a new test site had to be found. Whenever the engine was started, the noise and general commotion caused an almost complete stoppage of work in other parts of the plant. At length, the Power Jets organization rented what had once been on iron foundry at Lutterworth and transferred operations there. A complete reconstruction of the engine now began. And when the turbine in the new model failed, the engine had to be rebuilt a second time.

Whittle began running tests of this engine in October of 1938. Finances were still a critical problem, and there was not even enough money to replace engine parts which became damaged and distorted during testing. The strain of trying to perfect the engine in spite of every obstacle was beginning to affect Whittle's health, and he was plagued by frequent and severe headaches and indigestion.

On September 1, 1939, Germany invaded Poland. Britain and France immediately declared war on Germany. World War II was at hand. The official attitude toward Whittle's project shifted almost at once. Government leaders judged the turbojet engine vital to the war effort, and designated it to be added to the list of potential "war winning devices."

The Air Ministry now made valuable contributions to the Power Jets' staff in the way of engineering talent. The purse strings were loosened a bit. Another step forward took place when the Gloster Aircraft Company Ltd. was awarded a government contract to produce an experimental plane in which Whittle's engine could be tested.

By the spring of 1941, all was ready for the test flight. Whittle and his organization had developed a more sophisticated engine based on earlier experimental models, and after it had been bench-tested, it was installed in the Gloster-built aircraft, which had been dubbed the E.28. The RAF's field at Cranwell, with its long runway and clear approaches, was designated as the test site. P.E.G. (Gerry Sayer, Gloster's chief test pilot, was to be at the controls.

May 15, 1941, was set as the date for the test flight. The day dawned gray with low-hanging clouds and it was decided to cancel the flight. But late in the afternoon, the cloud cover lifted and there were patches of blue sky.

When the go ahead was given, Sayer eased the plane into position at the far eastern end of the runway. He marvelled at the absence of vibration, the steady hum instead of a thunderous roar, and the absence of complicated instrumentation. At 7:40 P.M., Sayer signalled he was ready.

He ran the engine up to 16,500 r.p.m., and then released the brakes. The handsome little plane raced smoothly down the runway, and after a run of about six hundred yards it lifted effortlessly into the evening sky.

"Frank, it flies!," a colleague shouted. "It flies!" And he slapped Whittle on the back in his joy.

Whittle, although tense, had no fears for his engine. "That's what it was designed to do, wasn't it?" he answered.

Sayer put the craft into a flat climb of several miles, and it disappeared into a cloudbank. Whittle and the other observers could hear only the steady drone of the engine. Then the plane came into sight again as Sayer circled the field wide to land.

The test pilot's approach was masterful. He glided the E.28 through a series of gentle turns, bringing the plane lower and lower. Said Whittle afterwards: "Those of us who were pilots knew that he felt completely at home."

Sayer's landing was perfect, and he taxied to a stop not far from where Whittle and the others were standing. Then he smiled broadly and gave the "thumbs up" sign. Everyone rushed forward to shake his hand and clap him on the back. Indeed, congratulations were in order. That seventeen-minute flight was a significant step into the jet age.

Despite the momentous nature of the event, little was done to form a detailed account of what had taken place. Whittle, usually meticulous in his record-keeping, did not look upon the test flight as especially significant at the time. The short hops that the airplane had made during taxi runs a few days before had dispelled any doubts he might have had that the plane would fly. Also, he looked upon the E.28 as purely an experimental plane, and, as such, not one that was going to be put into production to serve the Allied war effort. It must be said that Whittle's prime concern at the time was getting a more advanced version of the engine into production, one that was ultimately to provide the power for the RAF's "Meteor."

The photographic record of the E.28's first flight is sketchy at best. No one was able to persuade the Air Ministry to provide a motion picture crew to document the event. Someone using a hand-held movie camera did film the flight but according to Whittle the product was "a very amateur effort." Two still-photographs were taken, but the results were equally disappointing.

Over the next twelve days, the E.28 was test-flown a total of ten hours, and not the slightest bit of trouble was experienced with either the plane or the engine. The craft attained a top speed of 370 m.p.h. during these tests—well above that of the "Spitfire," England's foremost fighter plane of the day.

Even though the E.28 was guarded day and night by security police, and only those holding special passes were allowed to within several hundred yards of its hangar, it was impossible to hide completely what was taking place. After all, this plane, when compared to conventional piston craft, was undeniably different. It was incredibly propellerless, and when its engine was started, it put forth a strange high-pitched whine. Little wonder what RAF personnel stationed at Cranwell had an uncommon interest in the plane.

Observers could only speculate on how it operated. One officer assured his men that the E.28 was powered by a Rolls-Royce Merlin engine which drove a four-bladed propeller inside the fuselage. The officer stated positively that he had seen it. A civilian who had observed the E.28 in a test flight swore that the plane had shot straight upwards amidst a convulsive burst of fire and smoke. (No flame ever jetted out of the plane's tail pipe, and the smoke it emitted was barely visible.)

One day two officers were watching the E.28 take off, and their conversation was overheard by a member of the Power Jets staff. "How does that thing work?" said one of the men. "Oh, that's easy, old boy," answered his companion, "it just sucks itself along like a vacuum cleaner."

By now, all of Great Britain's aircraft manufacturing companies had become interested in the Whittle project. In the years that followed, two of these companies, Rolls-Royce, which used a direct descendant of an early Whittle model, and the de Havilland Company, were to become world leaders in production of aircraft gas turbine jets.

With the advent of the jet age, the sky began to shrink. History has recorded the swift and sweeping changes that took place.

This story is one more illustration. Whittle himself finally got to fly a jet plane for the first time in 1945. Later, in a Meteor III, Whittle took the ship through a high speed course marked by a line of buoys spaced a few hundred yards from the low cliffs which border the Thames Estuary east of Herne Bay. He first approached the course from the eastern end, diving down to the beginning of the run from a height of 1,500-feet with the throttles wide open. He leveled out at approximately fifty feet and covered the three kilometers in about fifteen seconds. He then climbed, made a wide turn, and covered the course from the opposite direction. He was too occupied watching where he was going during the runs to check his instruments, but he guessed he must have hit about 450 m.p.h.

It was an exhilarating experience for Whittle, and when he returned home, he recounted the event for his family.

"What speed did you do, Daddy?" asked his younger son, then eleven.

"About 450 m.p.h., I should think," Whittle answered.

The boy scowled, obviously disappointed. "What," he said, "only 450 m.p.h.?"

Here was a great irony. Aviation had advanced so far and so fast that Frank Whittle, the man most responsible for that advance, had been outstripped by it.

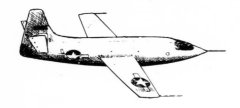

CHAPTER 13
THROUGH THE SOUND BARRIER

American military pilots of the 1940's called it "the brick wall in the sky." They were referring, of course, to the sound "barrier." For almost a decade it was thought to be every bit as insurmountable to an airplane as a thick steel wall would be to an automobile.

Pilots brought back frightening stories of what happened to them and their aircraft when they approached sonic speeds. One pilot who survived a power dive from 35,000 feet in a Republic P-47 reported that his control stick froze at 30,000 feet, and only by manually cranking the elevator trim tabs could he bring the ship out of the plunge. When the plane finally leveled out, the pilot said he felt "as though I'd been hit by a truck."

Less fortunate planes were know to have nosed down and found it impossible to level out. Some planes were said to have come apart in mid-air. Pilots were reported to have blacked out. Indeed, it was a mysterious and frightening world.

Because of these experiences, most pilots and many aeronautical engineers did not believe that the speed of sound would ever be attained, not by an airplane anyway. A missile might do it, they said, but the shock waves encountered as one approached sonic speed were so violent they would tear any plane to pieces. And even if a plane could be built to withstand the buffeting, what about the pilot? Could he survive?

The speed of sound is approximately 760 m.p.h. at sea

level at normal temperature. However, the speed of sound varies depending on the altitude and temperature. In the extremely cold air found at 36,000 feet, the speed of sound may be as low as 660 m.p.h. Near sea level in warm air, the speed can be as great as 790 m.p.h. Because of this variance, airmen express a plane's speed in a "Mach" number, which is the ratio of the speed of the airplane to the speed of sound in the surrounding atmosphere. Thus, a plane at Mach 1 is traveling at the speed of sound, no matter the altitude or temperature. Mach .75 is three-fourths of the speed of sound. Mach 2 is twice the speed of sound.

When the first jet engines were developed, since they provided so much more power than piston engines, the next step was obvious. "A high speed research airplane should be built," said Robert Wolf, assistant chief design engineer for the Bell Aircraft Corporation, the company that had built and successfully flown the first jet aircraft in the United States. "With such a plane," Wolf said, "we could explore the transonic range and find out what causes buffeting. Perhaps we could even fly beyond these speeds."

Wind tunnels of the day were not adequate when it came to furnishing high speed flight data. When air was pumped through a tunnel at close to the speed of sound, the tunnel underwent a bizarre reaction. It "choked" and its flow pattern became distorted.

A plane it would have to be. Late in 1944, the U.S. Army Air Corps and Bell Aircraft agreed to develop a ship that would be capable of exceeding the speed of sound.

A rugged set of specifications was drawn up. The plane would have to be able to carry hundreds of pounds of scientific equipment—cameras, recorders and telemetering devices to register such things as stick forces, airfoil pressure distribution and angular velocities. The pilot was to have full control of the ship's speed, and it would be his decision whether to take the plane through the "barrier." While the plane would have to be something of a flying laboratory, it would also have to be a practical ship for the military hoped that the craft would serve as a model for a plane capable of combat assignment.

Bell designed and built such a plane. They called it the X-1. Solid and strong, it was a small bullet-shaped plane of conventional mid-wing design. The wing, while extremely thin, was machined out of solid aluminum plate and had strength enough to carry a plane equal in weight to a B-36, the Air Force's long range heavy bomber. The X-1's tail and stabilizer sections were set unusually high so as to be above the wing wake and thereby serve to reduce buffeting.

The X-1 did not take off from a landing strip like a conventional airplane. Instead, it was carried aloft trussed to the belly of a B-29 *Superfortress*, the largest bomber of World War II. Then it was released.

The power plant consisted of four 1,500-pound thrust rockets which were fueled by a mixture of liquid oxygen and alcohol, a combination almost as explosive as dynamite. Engineers claimed that the plane was capable of speeds of up to Mach 2, and was strong enough to withstand 18 G's, or eighteen times the force of gravity.

Early in 1947, the X-1 was test flown by civilian pilots. It had attained a speed of Mach .8. Now it was ready to go beyond.

The Air Force launched a diligent search for a pilot to do the job. He would have to be alert, eager and reliable, besides being a pilot of extraordinary skill. He would also have to have stability, a very important quality. "He has to be unexcitable," said one Air Force officer, "just as solid as a building, just as stable as a rock."

Charles (Chuck) Yeager was born in Hamlin, a town of about 1,200, amidst the woods and rocky hills of southwestern West Virginia. The family had a small farm, and young Chuck and his brother Roy were skilled in weeding the garden and milking cows. He hunted and fished, and played tops and marbles. He merely tolerated school. Except at mathematics, he was not the best student. He liked all sports. In high school he played baseball and football and was a trombonist in the band. He read Mark Twain, the Tom Swift stories and the novels of Jack London. *The Call of the Wild* and *White Fang* were his favorites. Flying? He knew little about it.

"Hamlin is a good town to grow up in," his father once told him, "but that's all it is." Chuck was a restless young man, and his father advised him to move on. He wanted Chuck to go to college but there was no money to send him.

Chuck graduated from high school in the spring of 1941. He was eighteen. War was raging in Europe and Asia at the time, making more and more of an impression on Chuck. One day that summer, a friend of Chuck's named Jake Markham returned to Hamlin, after receiving training as an army pilot. "It's a good life," Jake said. "They send you to school. They train you. Then you've got a profession. And flying is fun. It's easy, and once you've flown you'll never want to do anything else."

Chuck was impressed. He talked it over with his parents. His father agreed it wasn't a bad idea. "They'll probably draft you anyway," he said. In September 1941, Chuck enlisted in the U.S. Army Air Corps.

The Army sent Chuck to mechanics' school, and six months passed before he even got to ride in a plane. One day while he was stationed at the Victorville, California, Army Air Base, an engineering officer asked him if he'd like to go along on a maintenance hop. When the plane reached proper flying altitude, Chuck looked down. He was not impressed. It was like standing on the edge of one of the cliffs back in West Virginia.

In August 1942, Chuck was sent to flying school. The classroom instruction was simple because he already knew all the mechanical systems of a plane. He knew how to run up the engines and taxi. He was a year ahead of most of the other trainees. But in the air, it was all new and different. Like the other trainees, Chuck learned to fly in a dual instruction plane. The pupil sat is the rear cockpit; the instructor was up front. Each had his own set of controls. Chuck had to concentrate every second.

In his first solo flight, Chuck's take off was perfect. He climbed to altitude, then leveled off. Everything was fine. Then he happened to catch a glimpse of the empty front seat and it frightened him. But he remembered the words of the instructor: "Do exactly as you'd do if I were sitting there." Chuck was still nervous when it became time for him to land. He put the plane down without a hitch. Just as the wheels touched the ground, he got a signal to take the plane up again. He landed a second time and again he was waved off. When he knew that he could do it, his anxiety disappeared. "Hey," he thought to himself, "this could be fun."

Chuck was a good student, cocky and eager, and willing to work hard. He learned gunnery and formation flying. He learned to do acrobatics. In March 1943, he received his wings and was assigned as a fighter pilot to the 375th Fighter Squadron. There was more training—in aerial gunnery, ground gunnery, dive bombing and skip bombing.

Early in January 1944, Chuck's squadron was assigned to the European Theater of Operations. In England, they were given new P-51 *Mustangs*. More classroom instruction and flight training followed.

Chuck's first combat mission came late in February, and it was filled with tension and excitement. When he arrived in the briefing shack, the first thing he noticed was a big wall map of Europe. A thin red line from England to Germany had been drawn upon it. His squadron was to provide escort for a fleet of heavy bombers, and the red line was the route they were to follow. Hamburg was to be the target.

"You'll find antiaircraft fire here," said the briefing officer, using a pointer, "and here and here and here and here." His pointer skipped about the map. "And you'll find some fighter opposition here." The pointer then defined a rectangular area over the Dutch channel coast.

But Chuck's first mission was uneventful. There were some scattered puffs of flak on the way to the target, and once over Hamburg, they became thicker, but they did not bother him. He searched the sky constantly for enemy aircraft but didn't see a single one. He watched the bombers deliver their payload, saw the bursts of smoke and flame below, and then watched them blend into one huge black cloud. Then it was back to England.

A few missions later, Chuck got his first German plane, an ME-109. On the same mission he shot up another aircraft. But the very next day, his fortune changed. His squadron was escorting a flight of bombers when they were pounced upon by FW-190's. Chuck, one of the first men to spot the enemy aircraft, flew head-on into them. "It seemed as if all of them hit him at once," said one witness. Chuck's engine caught fire, the elevator control was damaged and a gaping hole appeared in one wing. Chuck took flak fragments in both feet. He managed to get out, but he gashed open his head in the process. At 5,000 feet, he opened his chute.

Fortunately, Chuck was over southern France. Members of the French underground hid him from German patrols, and eventually passed him into Spain. It was a rugged journey. At the frontier, a buddy took a bullet in the knee. Chuck carried him to safety, an act of heroism that won his the Bronze Star.

Once back in England, Chuck learned that he was going to be sent back to the United States. It was policy. Any flier who had escaped the clutches of the Germans with the help of the French, was not allowed to return to combat, at least in the European Theater. The military feared that should the pilot fall into German hands a second time, he would be made to reveal how he had escaped and the names of the people who helped him. They would be shot.

Chuck protested the policy. "I'd feel terrible if I had to go back and start over again," he said. "It doesn't seem fair." At length, the military relented. Chuck was reassigned to his squadron and allowed to fly combat missions again.

Day after day the missions continued. Many times Chuck's courage and flying ability were commended. When it was over, he owned an extraordinary record: He had flown sixty-four combat missions. He had destroyed eleven enemy aircraft, shared a twelfth with a squadron buddy, and damaged three others in the air. Besides the Bronze Star, he had been awarded the Silver Star with an Oak Leaf Cluster, the Distinguished Fying Cross, the Air Medal with six Oak Leaf Clusters, the Purple Heart and the Presidential Unit Citation with which his squadron had been decorated.

Chuck came home and got married. He was assigned to Wright Field in Dayton, Ohio, as a test pilot. He was gratified to learn that most of the other pilots in the group were not quite so skilled in the air as he was, although they enjoyed higher rank.

Early in June 1947, the head of the Fighter Test Section assembled his men for an important announcement. The Air Force had taken over the X-1 project, he told them, and planned to assign one of their pilots to test the craft and take it beyond the speed of sound. He asked who would like to be considered for the job. Most of the men raised their hands, including Chuck. It was the beginning.

Chuck felt that his chances of winning the assignment were mighty slim. He held a temporary commission as a mere captain, while most of the other pilots were men of higher rank. He was skilled in dogfighting, and he had flown in some air shows, but that was the extent of his experience. Besides, he figured that being married and the father of two sons would weigh against him.

Of the 125 pilots of the Fighter Test Section, the military selected 25 men whom they believed to be qualified for the task. The records of each were carefully scrutinized, and they were subjected to lengthy personal interviews.

At one such interview, Chuck was asked if he believed that a plane could fly at sonic speeds.

"Yes, sir," he answered, and he said it as if he meant it. "I've fired many types of rifles," he explained, "and even a .22 caliber bullet travels faster than the speed of sound. You can fire into the water, and then recover the bullet. It's never distorted by the speed alone.

"I don't believe that speed is an obstacle—if you take it a little at a time," he added.

At another interview Chuck was told: "This *is not* a safe project. There are many risks. Don't you believe that having a family adds to your worry, and thereby increases your risk?"

Chuck had been waiting for that one. "Being married and having a family is a point in my favor," he said. "It's made me a more careful pilot."

Late in 1947, the Air Force told Chuck he was to be the man. "You're the pilot. It's up to you," he was told. "You have a tremendous responsibility. But safety is to be the prime factor. Nothing else matters. Is that clear?

Chuck was immediately assigned to Edwards Air Force Base at Muroc, California, and the X-1, mated to its B-29, was flown out. It was back to the classroom for Chuck. He spent week after week learning how the X-1 was put together and how it flew. He learned the function of every single part in the plane's air frame and power plant.

Days of preparation were to go into each actual powered flight. "A typical flight begins," Chuck was told, "the moment the last flight ends." Before a flight the plane had to be thoroughly inspected and its engine tested on the ground. Then it was linked to the B-29, fueled and its nitrogen system pressurized.

The procedure for doing all of these things was set down in careful detail. Each of the ten men in the X-1 ground crew and each man in the B-29 crew received a checklist outlining his duties. Then the men rehearsed, just the way a cast rehearses a play.

Chuck's first flight in the X-1 was a simple glide flight. The B-29 carried Chuck and the X-1 to an altitude of about 5,000 feet. Then he entered the bomb bay of the mother ship and lowered himself on a small steel ladder to the cabin door of the X-1. It was a hair-raising descent. The wind lashed at him and the roar of the B-29's engines blotted out every sound.

He squirmed through the open hatch. Once in his seat, he straightened his parachute and fastened his safety belt. Then he donned his helmet and breathing mask and hooked the mask into the oxygen supply system. The cockpit door was lowered to him from above. He caught it, fitted it into place and sealed it from within. Meanwhile, the B-29 was still climbing.

Chuck plugged in his radio, putting himself in contact with the B-29 pilot, the flight engineer, the pilots of the two chase planes and the control tower. He checked with each one. "How do you read me?" he asked.

"Fine," or "I read you loud and clear," came back the answers.

With this, Chuck began a meticulous check of his equipment. Was the landing gear handle in an "up" position? Was there adequate oxygen breathing pressure? Was the voltage supply sufficient? Was the cabin pressure valve in the "pressurized" position? Was the bail-out bottle (an emergency supply of oxygen) strapped to his leg?

"Completed my check," he reported.

There was nothing to do until the drop. It was cold and dark. Once more he checked the stick to be certain that it was in neutral position, the proper position for the drop. Then he checked it again.

"Three minutes," he was told.

He gave the controls a final check. He peered out the hatch. On either side he saw only the spinning props of the B-29's engines, not a comforting sight.

"Two minutes to drop," Chuck was told.

"Everything all right?" asked the flight engineer.

"Fine. Everything's fine," he answered. And he hoped his voice hadn't revealed his anxiety.

Then the countdown began. "Ten—nine—eight—seven . . ." Chuck's body braced for the drop. ". . . Six—five—four—three . . ." His hands tightened on the controls.

". . . Three—two—one. Drop!"

There was a dull, heavy sound, like the thump an ax makes when it strikes a thick pine. For an instant Church was weightless. His hands gripped the stick. Then his body sank down into the seat again as the X-1 began to glide.

Now he was flying, following the flight plan strapped to his knee. The long glide down to the dry lake bed thrilled him. It was easy; the plane almost landed itself.

"How was it?" he was asked when he got back on the ground.

"Best plane I've ever flown," he answered.

There were several such glide flights and then came the first powered flight. Its purpose was to simply familiarize Chuck with the handling characteristics of the plane under power. He was instructed to fly at moderate speed. "Don't exceed .82 Mach," he was told.

After the X-1 was loaded into the B-29, its nitrogen system was pressurized, and then its tanks were filled with fuel and liquid oxygen. The preflight inspection, the take off in the B-29 and the climb to altitude followed. The predrop check was more elaborate, for the fuel pressure had to be checked in each one of both rocket stages.

"I'm ready to drop," Chuck announced. Shortly after, the countdown began.

". . . three—two—one. Drop!"

At first, Chuck simply glided. Then in rapid sequence he flipped the four switches that ignite the cylinders. The plane shot ahead. Daringly, Chuck put it into a slow roll.

There were official spectators from the Air Material Command watching the flight from the control tower. Chuck took the X-1 down to 6,000 feet, leveled off over the tower, and then began a shallow climb.

Suddenly he was seized by a strange impishness. Only the first chamber was running, but he fired two, three and four in rapid succession. The plane streaked straight upward like a rocket from its pad. As he approached 30,000 feet, Chuck dropped the plane's nose slightly. The Mach meter registered .83. No human had ever flown so fast—and lived to tell of it. Then Chuck hit Mach .85. There was some slight buffeting, but otherwise everything was perfect.

There were mixed feeling over the flight. Some of the project engineers applauded Chuck's boldness in going to Mach .85, despite the fact he was told not to exceed .82. Others were distressed by what he had done. His Air Force superiors asked for an official explanation.

"Why did you do it?" a friend asked him.

"I don't know," Chuck answered. "I really don't know. Except that it's such a wonderful plane to fly, and I just wanted to fly it."

In the weeks that followed, the project settled into a routine. After the initial flight, several more flights were made in the Mach .80 to .88 range. Then Chuck made a level run at Mach .925. He was probing deeper and deeper into the unknown. "What's going to happen next?" was the question on everyone's lips.

On the next flight, Chuck took the X-1 to 40,000 feet and his speed hit Mach .94. The plane showed a high degree of stability. There was little buffeting and no roll. That night it was learned that special equipment monitoring the flight had calculated his speed to be Mach .99, not .94. "It looks as if the next flight will do it," Chuck was told.

October 14, 1947, was to be the day. Chuck arrived at the base shortly before six A.M. The B-29 and X-1 were made ready. The endless checking and rechecking began. "Don't go beyond Mach .96," Chuck was instructed, "unless you're absolutely sure that you can handle it."

The B-29 rolled down the runway and lifted gracefully into the air.

The procedure was the same, but Chuck felt the tension. His heart beat faster. His muscles tautened. The bomber climbed to altitude. Chuck walked back to the bomb bay, then climbed down the ladder and into the X-1. He settled into the seat. He adjusted his helmet and mask, then turned to seal the door shut. He plugged in his radio and began his first instrument check. So far it was like all the other flights.

"Three minutes to drop," he was told.

"You all set?" the engineer asked.

"Yes," Chuck answered. "Let's get this thing over with."

When the B-29 reached 20,000, the X-1 was released. Chuck glided briefly, then fired the rockets. He headed the plane straight up and watched the Mach meter intently—.83, .88, .92.

The needle climbed to .96, then .98. Suddenly the needle jumped right off the scale. "That's it!" Chuck thought. But there was no shock, no jolt, only some slight buffeting. Chuck was certain he had gone beyond the speed of sound. He estimated that he had hit Mach 1.05.

He began the long glide back to the base. He smiled to himself as he watched the Mach needle come back onto the scale. As he came in to land, he felt a sudden weariness, a release of all his pent up emotions.

Chuck was dead tired when he left the plane and asked permission to skip the debriefing until he could get some sleep. The news of his feat had spread, however, and soon he was the center of attention. The public address system made it official. "Attention all personnel," it blared, "The Bell X-1, piloted by Captain Charles Yeager, has just completed the first supersonic flight."

Chuck Yeager showed there was no "barrier," no "brick wall in the sky." This and other information derived from the X-1 flights paved the way for a whole new generation of supersonic aircraft. For years, Yeager's flight ranked as the ultimate. Nothing before was its equal. And its pre-eminence was not diminished until the early 1960's when Russia and the United States began making manned orbital space flights.

CHAPTER 14
LADY IN A JET

On a clear May morning in May 1953, at Edwards Air Force base near Muroc, California, Jacqueline Cochran Odlum tucked her honey-blonde hair into a gleaming red crash helmet, and climbed into the seat of a sleek Canadian-built North American F-86. Her aim was to try to break the world's 100-kilometer speed record. Much of her life had been spent proving that aviation was not solely a man's world. Now this remarkable woman was out to show that sex was no barrier to jet age flight.

In early 1950's, the fraternity of jet test pilots was as exclusively male as a football team. There were no commercial jet planes being built, and those that did exist belonged to the armed forces, so it was a rare thing for a woman to even fly a jet, let alone make a try for a speed record in one. But Jackie Cochran was a daring and determined woman. She never learned the meaning of the word "impossible."

Jackie was orphaned at the age of four and grew up amidst the poverty of the small sawmill towns of northern Florida. Her dresses were made of flour sacks; her bed was a straw-filled mattress on the floor. She had no shoes until she was eight. When the family she lived with moved to Columbus, Georgia, Jackie went to work in a cotton mill. Her job was to push a four-wheeled cart between the rows of looms in the weaving room, delivering bobbins to the workers. She worked twelve hours a

day and earned $4.50 a week. When she was ten, Jackie went to work in a beauty shop. She ran errands, did odd jobs and learned the skills of a beauty shop operator. At fourteen, she became a "permanent wave" operator in a beauty shop in Montgomery, Alabama.

As for Jackie's formal education, there was almost none to speak of. She was enrolled in the first grade in a Bagdad, Florida, school, but on the third day of class she was "rulered" by the teacher and abruptly dropped out. She did not return until the next year. A new teacher taught her how to read, and she began to devour newspapers, magazines and books. But at eight she went to work in the mill and never saw the inside of a classroom again.

When she was sixteen and living in Montgomery, Alabama, a friend persuaded her to enter nursing training. Three years later she returned to "sawdust road," as she called the sawmill towns of northern Florida, and took a job with a country doctor in Bonifay. She did not remain a mill-town nurse for very long. "I had neither the strength nor the money to do the smallest fraction of what had to be done for those people . . ." she was to write in later years. She moved on to become a partner in a beauty shop in Pensacola, Florida.

Jackie has said many times she has "itchy feet." This period of her life confirms it. She went to Philadelphia, spent almost a year there, and then moved to New York. There she managed to get a job at Antoine's swank beauty salon. During the winter months, she worked at Antoine's shop in Miami Beach. She was extremely popular and often her wealthy female patrons invited her to their parties. One night she was introduced to wealthy Floyd Odlum, a financier. Jackie confessed to him that she had wearied of her work as a beauty shop operator, and

155

told him she hoped to take a selling job with a cosmetics firm, traveling throughout the United States. Odlum smiled. With that kind of a territory," he said, "you'll need wings."

The statement started Jackie's mind churning. She decided that if she learned how to fly, she could become the national sales representative of just about any cosmetics firm she chose. One summer day in 1932, she drove out to Roosevelt Field on Long Island and inquired about flight instruction.

The first lesson was free—a teaser. The instructor was named Husky Lewellyn. "And he *was* Husky," Jackie once recalled. "He was so big he could hardly get into the plane. I wondered if it would carry us both." Husky didn't bother to explain a thing, just opened the throttle and took off. Once in the air he showed Jackie how to move the control stick to climb, dive or turn. Then he turned over the controls to her. "For some unknown reason, I caught on pretty well," Jackie said. On that day America's foremost woman flyer was born.

On her third day of flight instruction, Jackie soloed. Within three week's time she had taken her examination and received her license. Flying opened a whole new world for her. She gave up her job with Antoine and, with a rented plane, decided to attend an air meet for sportsmen pilots in Montreal. "Just follow the Hudson River until you get to Lake Champlain," a friend told her. "Then follow the lake to Burlington, Vermont. Land, clear customs and ask directions."

She managed to make Burlington without any serious problems. There the airport manager gave her the compass course and distance to Montreal. Jackie had to confess she didn't know how to read a compass. The airport manager was dumbfounded. He got a group of men together and they pushed the airplane around in a circle to get the compass needle to move, and at the same time the manager explained the various readings to Jackie. When she finally arrived at Montreal, Jackie was given a hero's welcome. She had completed a long distance flight and crossed an international border, both singular achievements for a woman flyer in the early 1930's.

During this period in aviation, forced landings were common because engines so lacked in efficiency. A pilot had to be constantly on the lookout for a place to put down. Jackie, while attending the Ryan Flying School in San Diego in the fall of 1932, admitted that she had landed "on a substantial part of all the beaches and open spots in Southern California." She once made a forced landing on a beach in Mexico with the head of the flying school as her passenger. Another time, in trying to set her plane down on a small field, she went through a fence, onto a road, and slammed into a parked car owned by a traffic judge. He fined her twenty-five dollars for illegal parking.

Obtaining advanced flying instruction was no easy matter. Jackie got Wiley Post, a noted aviator of the day, to teach her some of the basics of instrument flying. When Post became involved in planning his around-the-world flight, Jackie tried to teach herself the art, attempting to fly with her face covered by a hood. A student flier would sit in the cockpit with her and keep a careful watch for other aircraft and advise her on the plane's attitude.

She also worked out a scheme that enabled her to get experience flying big passenger planes. In the early days of commercial aviation, there were no stewardesses to serve meals or look after the comforts of the passengers. These chores were left to the co-pilot. All co-pilots detested the work. Jackie would arrange with a co-pilot to attend to the cabin duties. She won rank as commercial aviation's first stewardess.

Jackie saw Floyd Odlum often. He continued to encourage her to fly. They were married on May 11, 1936. Odlum at the time was known as the "Wizard of Wall Street" because of his genius in restoring ailing businesses to good health. Both he and Jackie had fallen in love with the Coachella Valley of California and both owned property there. Jackie had twenty acres, her husband had a thousand acres. Nevertheless, when they merged their holdings Jackie received top billing. It was known as the Cochran-Odlum ranch. By this time Jackie had established her own cosmetics business and it was thriving, providing her with both the finances and leisure time to pursue her interests as a pilot.

In 1937, Jackie made headlines by placing third in the Vincent Bendix Trophy race, a transcontinental (Los Angeles to Cleveland) speed race. She was first among women contestants. In the same year, she established a women's national speed record of 292.27 m.p.h.

In the 1938 Bendix, piloting a Seversky P-35, Jackie finished first, defeating a field of nine men. She not only displayed immense flying skill, but also provoking femininity. While officials, newspaper reporters and spectators waited anxiously for her to appear at the judges' stand, Jackie remained in the cockpit, making repairs to her makeup and coiffure. Her time for the flight from Burbank to Cleveland was 8 hours, 10 minutes, and 31.4 seconds. After winning, she flew on to the East Coast to establish a transcontinental record.

The Harmon Trophy is given annually by the *Ligue Internationale des Aviateurs* for the year's most splendid aviation achievement. No one was surprised when Miss Cochran was voted the award in 1937 and again in 1938. But she continued to win it every year through 1950. When World War II broke out, there were only three other women in the world—one a Frenchwoman, the other two Russians—who held more international records than Miss Cochran.

She put her knowledge and experience to good use during the war. The United States needed women pilots for aircraft ferrying missions, and in 1942 an organization known as the Women's Air Force Service Pilots—or WASPS—was established to supply them. General H. H. Arnold, commanding general of the Air Force, appointed Miss Cochran the organization's director. Specifically, her job was to prepare a pool of trained women fliers for ferrying assignment. She waged a constant war of her own to win Air Force officer status for her pilots. The matter eventually came before Congress and was voted down, a rare defeat for Miss Cochran. By the end of the war, more than one-thousand women had received training as WASPS. Miss Cochran was awarded the Distinguished Service Medal for her work. The WASPS were disbanded in 1945.

After World War II, Jackie purchased a war-surplus North American P-51, the leading U.S. single-seat fighter during the war. She modified it for racing and set a world speed record with the ship. She placed second in the Bendix in 1946 and third in 1948. But piston craft were on the way out, at least when it came to record speeds. Air Force Colonel Al Boyd had piloted a lockheed P-80 Shooting Star at over 620 m.p.h. In 1944,

Jackie had been given a short flight in the Bell-P-59, but now she wanted to fly a jet—to become the first woman to do so. She began knocking on doors. The answer she got was "sorry." The fastest jets of the day belonged to the armed services and were not available for private flying. The fact that Jackie held a commission as a Lieutenant Colonel in the U.S. Air Force Reserve didn't help any.

In 1951, the women's speed record that Jackie had held was broken by Jacqueline Auriol of France. The chic and glamorous Mme. Auriol, daughter-in-law of the President of the French Republic, blazed a French Air Force de Havilland *Vampire* over a 100-kilometer course at a speed of 507 m.p.h. The next year she broke the record with a 530 m.p.h. performance. Jackie, of course, was anxious to win back the record, but her attempts to get her hands on the controls of a jet plane again met with failure.

One day in 1951, Jackie watched as Air Force Colonel Fred Ascani set a world's speed record for the 100-kilometer run. He hit 635 m.p.h. After the flight Jackie congratulated him.

"You could do better, Jackie," Ascani said.

Jackie shrugged. "There's not a chance," she said. "I can't get a plane."

"Maybe you can't get an American jet," the colonel replied, "But what about a Canadian one." Then he explained how Canadair, Ltd., a division of the General Dynamics Company, planned to build a version of the F-86 *Sabre*, and equip it with a powerful Orenda engine. "With that plane you could beat my record by fifteen miles an hour," Ascani said.

Jackie needed no further encouragement. Within a few months she landed a job with Canadair as a flight consultant, with the understanding that she would be able to put the plane through speed tests before it was turned over to the Canadian Air Force. When she learned that the plane was to be sent to Edwards Air Force base in the California desert for other tests, she made arrangements to do her speed trials there.

The *Sabre*, like any sophisticated jet craft, is a complicated instrument, and painstaking preparation is necessary to fly one. Jackie spent weeks studying the pilots' operating manual, attempting to learn in a short time what the average test pilot is taught in a year or more of instruction. She once calculated that for every hour of flying time she spent in the *Sabre*, there were over one-hundred hours spent in ground work.

She made five short flights in the *Sabre* before her attempt at the speed record. The first time she flew the plane she took it to 30,000 feet and put it into a gentle dive. She hit .97 of Mach 1. The next day she went to Mach .99. During the flight, Chuck Yeager, who was acting as Jackie's instructor and stayed close to her in a trail plane, told her to look at his plane and tell him what she observed. She could actually see the shock waves rolling off the canopy of Chuck's jet, just the way a film of water runs down a window pane on a rainy day. Atmospheric conditions have to be just right for a pilot to be able to see the shock waves as well as feel them.

On her climb to high altitude, Jackie crossed the Mexican border, and on the way back she crossed over the Cochran-Odlum ranch. To say "hello" to her husband she left a contrail in the sky which forms when the hot exhaust gases from a jet strike the freezing air found at high altitude, and the water vapor in them is condensed into ice crystals. To observers on the ground, the plane seems to be emitting an endless ribbon of white gossamer.

On her next flight, Jackie was determined to break the sonic barrier. Only Chuck Yeager knew of her plans.

The day came. She climbed the plane to 45,000-feet higher than she had ever been before. She noticed the sky became darker and darker, and marveled that she could see the stars even though it was midday. She leveled off, then put the plane into an S-shaped dive. She watched the needle on her Mach meter and reported the readings to Yeager. "Mach .97, Mach .98," she called out. Shock waves tore at the plane. The left wing dipped abruptly, then over-corrected. "Mach .99". The plane felt like it wanted to fly on its back. But she kept its nose pointed earthward. "Mach 1.0, Mach 1.01." Her face broke into a wide smile. She had done it! Another barrier was behind her.

Cautiously Jackie pulled out of the dive. She knew that she had to level off before she reached heavier air at 18,000-feet and below. In those regions a pull-out could tear a plane apart.

Her friends congratulated her when she landed. "I felt as if I were walking about ten feet above the ground," Jackie said. Then came the sad news that her feat had not been officially recorded. The control tower had not heard the sonic boom, the loud explosions that result when a plane breaks through the barrier. Jackie took the news calmly. "I'll do it again," she said. She climbed back into the plane.

This time she stayed with the dive until the Mach meter was well above Mach 1. The control tower recorded the explosions and also heard Jackie counting off the readings. This time it was official.

Jackie had neglected to wear a G-suit during her dives, an oversight that had unhappy results. When rocketing through the air at sonic speed, a pilot is subjected to G (or gravity) forces that exert tremendous pressure upon his body. Four G's, a pull four times that of gravity, can drain the blood from the brain into the abdominal cavity and legs, resulting in blindness and eventually blackout. A pilot wears a G-suit to constrict his lower body and delay the blood drain from his upper body. Jackie had been tested at the Mayo clinic a year before her flight and was told that she could withstand a pull of four G's for a short period without blacking out. She knew none of her flights would subject her to that amount of pressure. The G-suit is hot and uncomfortable to wear, and she noticed that Chuck Yeager had not donned one. "I can get along without one. Why bother?" she thought.

Two days later she was in a hospital at Albuquerque, New Mexico, as a result of her neglect. She was suffering from abdominal adhesions which caused sharp pains. For several days she slept with the foot of her bed raised fifteen inches, and breathed pure oxygen for three hours each night. When the pain subsided, she returned to Edwards and resumed her practice and training for the record attempts. But she never failed to wear a G-suit again.

Many of the people who were aware of what Jackie was planning doubted that she could break the 100-kilometer record. Her *Sabre* was capable of 675 m.p.h., but that was on an arrow-straight course over a short distance. The official 100-kilometer course is circular, marked off by twelve slender towers called pylons. All the pylons had to be passed on the outside, meaning Jackie would have to fly the plane at about a thirty-degree bank. There was an element of danger in that Jackie had to fly at the height of 300-feet, low enough to enable the photographic timing devices to document the plane's crossing of the start and finish points of the circuit. All in all, it was a tortuous test, calling for the ultimate in precision flying.

The Federation Aeronautique Internationale takes no chances when seeking to certify a record. Besides the photographic timing devices, two official observers were to be posted at each pylon. There were to be two panels of Judges, each equipped with electronic timing devices accurate to the ten-thousandth of a second. Chuck Yeager was to be aloft as an observer. Jackie knew she had to better Colonel Ascani's mark by at least one per cent in order to qualify for official recognition. That meant a speed of 642 m.p.h. was necessary.

On May 20, all was in readiness. The run had to be made in the late morning, after the air temperature had risen but before any turbulence began. There were mixed feelings when Jackie roared the silvery jet down the concrete runway and into the air. Few women had ever flown a jet plane. None had ever test-flown one; none had ever tried for a record in a jet. Chuck Yeager was confident that Jackie would be successful, and so was Lieutenant Colonel Pete Everest, chief of the test section at the Edwards base. There were others, however, that felt the test would be a failure, that Jackie would be lucky to hit 630 m.p.h. Some believed it might end in tragedy.

On her first run, Jackie achieved a speed of 652 m.p.h. The forty judges, timers and observers sprinkled about the course quickly affirmed a world's record had been set.

There were two more speed records that Jackie wanted—the 3 kilometer and the 15-kilometer—both over straight courses.

On June 2, she attempted the 3-kilometer run, going back and forth over the course four times. The air was somewhat turbulent, which increased the plane's tendency to roll. Yet Jackie had to maintain precise control over the plane. If she veered from the course by as little as 200-feet, she knew she would be out of camera range, and a film record was necessary for the run to be regarded as official.

When Jackie landed, she was told that four stopwatches had clocked her at a record 690 m.p.h., but she also got the report that the run was not to be considered official because the electronic timing equipment had malfunctioned.

Although disheartened, Jackie decided to try for the 15-kilometer record of 699 m.p.h. the next day. Two consecutive passes over the course in opposite directions were required. Jackie had enough fuel for four passes. On her first run, she attained a speed of 680 m.p.h. On the second pass, with the wind against her, she hit 670 m.p.h.

As she neared the end of the third pass, Jackie sought to level out, but the controls froze, and the plane went into a harrowing roll. Using both hands, and a knee for leverage, she struggled to right the plane, but it continued to bank. Another second or two and it would be on its back and into the ground. Quickly Jackie cut the speed. It worked. The plane rolled in the opposite direction and came right side up. Then she got a report that the plane had gyrated beyond the range of the timing cameras. There was no use continuing. She made a long turn to land.

Suddenly she spotted Chuck Yeager's plane close behind. His voice crackled into her ear. "Keep your hand off the throttle as much as you can," he ordered. "Set her down on the lake bed, and do it right away!" His voice was urgent. Something was up.

The alkaline lake beds adjacent to the Edwards Air Force base are as smooth and as hard as a block of polished marble. They are used mainly for emergency landings, when a pilot needs a long roll. She picked out one of the beds and circled to land. She flipped off her oxygen mask. The smell of fuel hit her.

The plane touched down. As it rolled to a stop, she heard Yeager's voice again. "Cut the throttle and switches, and get out of there!" he ordered. "You've got a fuel leak!" Yeager, in the trail plane, had spotted a stream of fuel gushing from her plane's left wing. An inspection disclosed that vibration plus the turbulent air had caused the fuel tank to rupture. If the fuel had seeped into the fuselage when the engine was *turning*, it would have caused a violent explosion. It was a close call. "It would have been the end of the plane and the end of me," Jackie said afterwards. "And somebody would surely have blamed it on the fact a woman was flying."

Jackie later broke her own speed record—and in spectacular fashion. In 1963, flying a Lockheed F-104, she became the first woman to fly at Mach 2, or twice the speed of sound.

In 1960, Jackie became the first woman to make an arrested jet landing on an aircraft carrier. The vessel was the USS Independence. She was also the first of her sex to be launched into the air by the carrier's high-powered steam catapult system. She said the experience felt like "having your backbone pushed through your body."

In April 1962, she made headlines with a jet again. With three companions, she took off from New Orleans in a Lockheed Jetstar, a plane powered by four rear-pod-mounted jet engines. She stopped for fuel at Gander, Newfoundland, and Ireland, and arrived at her destination, Hanover, Germany, approximately fourteen hours later. The journey set forty-nine new records, the bulk of them for flight times between various cities. For instance, it took her a mere 27 minutes, 7 seconds, to cover the distance from Washington to New York. The principal record that the flight set was a straight-line long distance mark between New Orleans and Gander.

More than anything else, Jackie Cochran's record setting performances in jet planes demonstrated that women "belonged" to the world of aviation of the 1960's and 1970's. That was her goal; she never swerved from it. As for the future, she says, "I will be there, cheering with my last breath those who are carrying on." No one doubts that she will be.

BIBLIOGRAPHY

Balchen, Bernt. *Come North With Me.* New York: E. P. Dutton & Co. 1927.

Brigole, Alexandre. *Santos-Dumont, Pioneer of the Air.* Rio de Janeiro: Aero Club of Brazil, 1941.

Cochran, Jacqueline. *The Stars at Noon.* Boston: Little, Brown and Co., 1954.

Donovan, Frank. *The Early Eagles.* New York: Dodd, Mead & Co., 1962.

Heiman, Grover. *Jet Pioneers.* New York: Duell, Sloan and Pearce, 1963.

Kelly, Fred C. *The Wright Brothers.* New York: Harcourt, Brace & Co., 1943.

Kingsford-Smith, C. E. and Ulm, C.T.P. *The Flight of the Southern Cross.* New York: National Travel Club, 1929.

Knight, Clayton and Durham, Robert. *Hitch Your Wagon, The Story of Bernt Balchen.* Drexel Hill, Penna.: Bell Publishing Co., 1950.

Lindbergh, Charles A. *"We".* New York: Grosset & Dunlap, 1927.

Mason, Herbert Malloy, Jr. *Bold Men, Far Horizons.* Philadelphia: J. P. Lippincott Co., 1966.

May, Charles Paul. *Women in Aeronautics.* New York: Thomas Nelson & Sons, 1962.

Mollison, James, Editor. *Book of Famous Flyers.* London: Collins' Clear-Type Press, 1934.

Orlob, Helen, *Daring Young Men in their Flying Machines.* New York: Thomas Nelson & Sons, 1960.

Post, Wiley and Gatty, Harold. *Around the World in Eight Days.* New York: Rand McNally & Co., 1931.

Sunderman, James F., Editor. *Early Air Pioneers.* New York: Franklin Watts, Inc. 1961.

Taylor, P. G. *Pacific Flight, The Story of the Lady Southern Cross.* Sydney: Angus & Robertson Ltd., 1937.

Whittle, Sir Frank. *Jet.* New York: Philosophical Library, Inc., 1954.

Wiggin, Charles S. *First Transcontinental Flight.* New York: The Book Mailer, 1961.

Wright, Orville. *How We Invented the Airplane.* New York: David McKay Co., Inc., 1953.

INDEX

They flew alone

DATE DUE
